Volume 2 (Chapters 14-19)

Student Solutions

for

CALCULUS AND ANALYTIC GEOMETRY
Second Edition

by Mizrahi and Sullivan

R. A. Fritz
Moraine Valley Community College

Richard Tucker
Mary Baldwin College

Thomas O'Neil
California Polytechnic State University
San Luis Obispo

Wadsworth Publishing Company
Belmont, California
A Division of Wadsworth, Inc.

Mathematics Editor: Jim Harrison
Editorial Coordinator: Anne Scanlan-Rohrer
Production: Matrix
Illustration: George Omura
Typist: Goolcher Wadia

Printed in the United States of America

1 2 3 4 5 6 7 8 9 10---90 89 88 87 86

ISBN 0-534-05457-9

CONTENTS

This solutions manual contains solutions to every
other odd-numbered problem.

Chapter Fourteen

Exercise 1, p. 743-744

3. $\vec{x} + \vec{B} = \vec{F} \implies \vec{x} = \vec{A}$

7. $\vec{E} = -\vec{G} - \vec{H} + \vec{D}$ (compare with Problem 4)

11. $\|\vec{V}\| = 3 \implies \|4\vec{V}\| = 4\|\vec{V}\| = 12$

Exercise 2, pp. 748-749

3. $\vec{V} = (-1-0)\vec{i} + (6-5)\vec{j} = -\vec{i} + \vec{j}$

7. $\|\vec{V}\| = \sqrt{4^2 + (-3)^2} = \sqrt{25} = 5$

11. $\|\vec{V}\| = \sqrt{a^2 + (-a)^2} = \sqrt{2a^2} = |a|\sqrt{2}$

15. $\frac{1}{3}\vec{V} + \frac{1}{2}\vec{W} = \frac{1}{3}(2\vec{i}-3\vec{j}) + \frac{1}{2}(\vec{i}+2\vec{j})$

$$= (\frac{2}{3}\vec{i} - \vec{j}) + (\frac{1}{2}\vec{i} + \vec{j}) = \frac{7}{6}\vec{i}$$

19. $\vec{U} = \frac{\vec{V}}{\|\vec{V}\|} = \frac{5\vec{i} - 12\vec{j}}{\sqrt{25 + 144}} = \frac{5}{13}\vec{i} - \frac{12}{13}\vec{j}$;

$-\vec{U} = \frac{-5}{13}\vec{i} + \frac{12}{13}\vec{j}$

23. $\vec{U} = \frac{\vec{V}}{\|\vec{V}\|} = \frac{\frac{1}{2}\vec{i} + \frac{\sqrt{3}}{2}\vec{j}}{\sqrt{\frac{1}{4} + \frac{3}{4}}} = \frac{1}{2}\vec{i} + \frac{\sqrt{3}}{2}\vec{j}$; $-\vec{U} = -\frac{1}{2}\vec{i} - \frac{\sqrt{3}}{2}\vec{j}$

27. $\vec{V} = a\vec{i} + b\vec{j}$, $\|\vec{V}\| = 5$, $a = 2b$

$\|V\| = \sqrt{a^2 + b^2} \implies 5 = \sqrt{(2b)^2 + b^2}$

$\implies 5 = \sqrt{5b^2} \implies \pm\sqrt{5} = b$

In this manual, an arrow over a letter or number represents a vector instead of the boldface notation used in the text.

$$\vec{V} = 2\sqrt{5}\vec{i} + \sqrt{5}\vec{j} \text{ or } -2\sqrt{5}\vec{i} - \sqrt{5}\vec{j}$$

31. As in Example 3, $\vec{v}_a = 500\vec{i}$

Vector going northwest = $-\vec{i} + \vec{j}$

Corresponding unit vector = $\dfrac{-\vec{i} + \vec{j}}{\|\vec{i} + \vec{j}\|} = \dfrac{-\vec{i} + \vec{j}}{\sqrt{1 + 1}}$

$$= \dfrac{1}{\sqrt{2}}(-\vec{i} + \vec{j})$$

Velocity of wind = $\vec{V}_w = 60 \cdot \dfrac{1}{\sqrt{2}}(-\vec{i} + \vec{j})$

$$= -30\sqrt{2}\ \vec{i} + 30\sqrt{2}\ \vec{j}$$

Velocity of plane relative to the ground = $\vec{V}_g$

$= \vec{V}_a + \vec{V}_w \Rightarrow \vec{V}_g = 500\vec{i} + (-30\sqrt{2}\ \vec{i} + 30\sqrt{2}\ \vec{j})$

$= (500 - 30\sqrt{2})\ \vec{i} + 30\sqrt{2}\ \vec{j}$

Speed = $\|V_g\| = \sqrt{(500 - 30\sqrt{2})^2 + (30\sqrt{2})^2} \approx 459.54$ km/hr

35. (a)

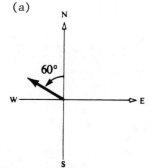

(b)

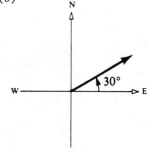

39. $\vec{V} + \vec{W} = 2\vec{i} - \vec{j} + x\vec{i} + 3\vec{j} = (2+x)\vec{i} + 2\vec{j}$

$\|\vec{V} + \vec{W}\| = 5 \Rightarrow \sqrt{(2+x)^2 + 2^2} = 5 \Rightarrow 4 + 4x + x^2 + 4 = 25$

$\Rightarrow x^2 + 4x - 17 = 0 \Rightarrow x = \dfrac{-4 \pm \sqrt{16 - 4(1)(-17)}}{2}$

$x = \dfrac{-4 \pm \sqrt{84}}{2} = -2 \pm \sqrt{21}$

<u>Exercise 3</u>, pp. 754-755

3.

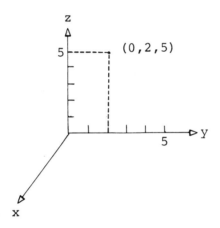

7. $(0,0,0)$, $(2,0,0)$, $(2,1,0)$, $(0,1,0)$

   $(0,0,3)$, $(2,0,3)$, $(2,1,3)$, $(0,1,3)$

11. $(-1,0,2)$, $(4,0,2)$, $(4,2,2)$, $(-1,2,2)$

    $(-1,0,5)$, $(4,0,5)$, $(4,2,5)$, $(-1,2,5)$

15. $x = 0 \Rightarrow$ yz-plane

19. $d = \sqrt{(4-1)^2 + (1-3)^2 + (2-0)^2} = \sqrt{9 + 4 + 4} \quad \sqrt{17}$

23. $d = \sqrt{(3-4)^2 + [2-(-2)]^2 + [1-(-2)]^2}$

    $= \sqrt{1 + 16 + 9} = \sqrt{26}$

For problems 25-28 use equation (14.7).

27. $[x - (-1)]^2 + (y-1)^2 + (z-2)^2 = 9$

    or $(x+1)^2 + (y-1)^2 + (z-2)^2 = 9$

31. $x^2 + y^2 + z^2 - 4x + 4y + 2z = 0 \Rightarrow$
    $(x^2-4x) + (y^2+4y) + (z^2+2z) = 0 \Rightarrow$
    $(x^2-4x+4) + (y^2+4y+4) + (z^2+2z+1) = 0 + 4 + 4 + 1 \Rightarrow$
    $(x-2)^2 + (y+2)^2 + (z+1)^2 = 9 \Rightarrow$
    center = $(2,-2,-1)$, radius = $\sqrt{9} = 3$

35. End points of a diameter are $(-2,0,4)$ and $(2,6,8)$

    $\Rightarrow$ Center = $(0,3,6)$ and

    radius = $\sqrt{(2-0)^2 + (6-3)^2 + (8-6)^2} = \sqrt{4 + 9 + 4} = \sqrt{17}$

    Sphere: $(x-0)^2 + (y-3)^2 + (z-6)^2 = (\sqrt{17})^2$

    or, $x^2 + (y-3)^2 + (z-6)^2 = 17$

39. $A = (-2,6,0)$, $B = (4,9,1)$, $C = (-3,2,18)$

    $|AB| = \sqrt{[4 - (-2)]^2 + (9-6)^2 + (1-0)^2} = \sqrt{36 + 9 + 1} = \sqrt{46}$

    $|AC| = \sqrt{[-3 - (-2)]^2 + (2-6)^2 + (18-0)^2} = \sqrt{1 + 16 + 324}$

    $= \sqrt{341}$

    $|BC| = \sqrt{(-3 - 4)^2 + (2-9)^2 + (18-1)^2} = \sqrt{49 + 49 + 289}$

    $= \sqrt{387}$

    Since $[|AB|]^2 + [|AC|]^2 = [|BC|]^2$, by the Pythagorean theorem $\triangle ABC$ is a right triangle (and BC is the hypotenuse).

43. $A = (2,4,2)$, $B = (2,1,5)$, $C = (5,1,2)$

    $|AB| = \sqrt{(2-2)^2 + (4-1)^2 + (2-5)^2} = \sqrt{18} = 3\sqrt{2}$

    $|AC| = \sqrt{(2-5)^2 + (4-1)^2 + (2-2)^2} = \sqrt{18} = 3\sqrt{2}$

    $|BC| = \sqrt{(2-5)^2 + (1-1)^2 + (5-2)^2} = \sqrt{18} = 3\sqrt{2}$

    Therefore, A, B, and C are the vertices of an equilateral triangle.

3. $\vec{V} = [2-(-1)]\vec{i} + (0-0)\vec{j} + (0-1)\vec{k} = 3\vec{i} - \vec{k}$

7. $3\vec{V} - 2\vec{W} = 3(3\vec{i} + \vec{j} - \vec{k}) - 2(6\vec{i} + \vec{j} + \vec{k})$
$$= 9\vec{i} + 3\vec{j} - 3\vec{k} - 12\vec{i} - 2\vec{j} - 2\vec{k} = -3\vec{i} + \vec{j} - 5\vec{k}$$

11. $2\vec{u} - 3\vec{v} + 4\vec{w} = 2(\vec{i} - 2\vec{j} + 3\vec{k})$
$$- 3(3\vec{i} + \vec{j} - \vec{k}) + 4(6\vec{i} + \vec{j} + \vec{k})$$
$$= 17\vec{i} - 3\vec{j} + 13\vec{k}$$

15. $\|\vec{u} + \vec{v} + \vec{w}\|$
$$= \|(\vec{i} - 2\vec{j} + 3\vec{k}) + (3\vec{i} + \vec{j} - \vec{k}) + (6\vec{i} + \vec{j} + \vec{k})\|$$
$$= \|10\vec{i} + 3\vec{k}\| = \sqrt{10^2 + 0^2 + 3^2} = \sqrt{109}$$

19. $\|\vec{V}\| = \|4\vec{i} + 2\vec{j} - \vec{k}\| = \sqrt{4^2 + 2^2 + (-1)^2} = \sqrt{21}$
$$\cos \alpha = \frac{a}{\|\vec{V}\|} = \frac{4}{\sqrt{21}}, \quad \cos \beta = \frac{b}{\|\vec{V}\|} = \frac{2}{\sqrt{21}},$$
$$\cos \gamma = \frac{c}{\|\vec{V}\|} = \frac{-1}{\sqrt{21}}$$

23. $\|\vec{V}\| = \|a\vec{i} + a\vec{j} + a\vec{k}\| = \sqrt{a^2 + a^2 + a^2} = a\sqrt{3}$, since
$a > 0$. $\cos \alpha = \dfrac{a}{\|\vec{V}\|} = \dfrac{a}{a\sqrt{3}} = \dfrac{1}{\sqrt{3}}$, $\quad \cos \beta = \dfrac{b}{\|\vec{V}\|} = \dfrac{a}{a\sqrt{3}}$
$= \dfrac{1}{\sqrt{3}}$, $\quad \cos \gamma = \dfrac{c}{\|\vec{V}\|} = \dfrac{a}{a\sqrt{3}} = \dfrac{1}{\sqrt{3}}$

27. $\alpha = \dfrac{\pi}{4} \Rightarrow \cos \alpha = \dfrac{\sqrt{2}}{2}$, $\gamma = \dfrac{\pi}{3} \Rightarrow \cos \gamma = \dfrac{1}{2}$. By

formula (14.10), $\cos^2\alpha + \cos^2\beta + \cos^2\gamma = 1 \Rightarrow$

$\dfrac{1}{2} + \cos^2\beta + \dfrac{1}{4} = 1 \Rightarrow \cos^2\beta = \dfrac{1}{4} \Rightarrow \cos \beta = \pm \dfrac{1}{2} \Rightarrow$

$\cos \beta = -\dfrac{1}{2}$ and $\beta = \dfrac{2\pi}{3}$, since $\dfrac{\pi}{2} < \beta < \pi$.

By formula (14.11),

$$\vec{V} = \|\vec{V}\| [(\cos \alpha)\vec{i} + (\cos \beta)\vec{j} + (\cos \gamma)\vec{k}]$$

$$= 2(\frac{\sqrt{2}}{2}\vec{i} + (-\frac{1}{2})\vec{j} + \frac{1}{2}\vec{k}) = \sqrt{2}\vec{i} - \vec{j} + \vec{k}$$

31. $\|2\vec{i} + \vec{j} - \vec{k}\| = \|2\alpha\vec{i} + \vec{j} + \vec{k}\| \Rightarrow \sqrt{4 + 1 + 1}$

$$= \sqrt{4\alpha^2 + 1 + 1} \Rightarrow \sqrt{6} = \sqrt{4\alpha^2 + 2} \Rightarrow 6 = 4\alpha^2 + 2$$

$$\Rightarrow 4\alpha^2 = 4 \Rightarrow \alpha^2 = 1 \Rightarrow \alpha = \pm 1$$

Exercise 5, 769-771

3. $\vec{V} \cdot \vec{W} = 1(0) - 1(1) + 0(1) = -1$, $\|\vec{V}\| = \sqrt{1 + 1 + 0} = \sqrt{2}$,

$\|\vec{W}\| = \sqrt{0 + 1 + 1} = \sqrt{2} \Rightarrow \cos \theta = \frac{\vec{V} \cdot \vec{W}}{\|\vec{V}\|\|\vec{W}\|} = \frac{-1}{\sqrt{2}\sqrt{2}} = -\frac{1}{2}$

7. From Problem 1, $\vec{V} \cdot \vec{W} = 6$, $\|\vec{W}\| = \sqrt{3} \Rightarrow$ projection

of $\vec{V}$ along $\vec{W} = \frac{\vec{V} \cdot \vec{W}}{\|\vec{W}\|} = \frac{6}{\sqrt{3}} = 2\sqrt{3}$

11. From Problem 5, $\vec{V} \cdot \vec{W} = -8$, $\|\vec{W}\| = \sqrt{6} \Rightarrow$ projection

of $\vec{V}$ along $\vec{W} = \frac{\vec{V} \cdot \vec{W}}{\|\vec{W}\|} = \frac{-8}{\sqrt{6}}$

15. $\vec{V} \cdot \vec{W} = 0 \Rightarrow \alpha(1) + 1(\alpha) + 1(4) = 2\alpha + 4 = 0 \Rightarrow \alpha = -2$

19. Projection of $\vec{V}$ along $\vec{i} = \frac{\vec{V} \cdot \vec{i}}{\|\vec{i}\|} = \vec{V} \cdot \vec{i}$, since

$\|\vec{i}\| = 1$. For $\vec{V} = a\vec{i} + b\vec{j} + c\vec{k}$, using formula (14.12),

$\vec{V} \cdot \vec{i} = a(1) + b(0) + c(0) = a$, $\vec{V} \cdot \vec{j} = a(0) + b(1)$

$+ c(0) = b$, and $\vec{V} \cdot \vec{k} = a(0) + b(0) + c(1) = c$.

Thus, $\vec{V} = (\vec{V} \cdot \vec{i})\vec{i} + (\vec{V} \cdot \vec{j})\vec{j} + (\vec{V} \cdot \vec{k})\vec{k}$.

23. $W = \vec{F} \cdot \vec{D} = (2\vec{i} - \vec{j} - \vec{k}) \cdot (3\vec{i} + 2\vec{j} - 5\vec{k})$

$$= 2(3) - 1(2) - 1(-5) = 9$$

27. Right triangle with right angle at $C \Rightarrow \overrightarrow{AC}$ and $\overrightarrow{BC}$

are orthogonal $\Rightarrow \overrightarrow{AC} \cdot \overrightarrow{BC} = 0 \Rightarrow$

$(-\vec{i} + 3\vec{j} + z\vec{k}) \cdot (2\vec{i} + 0\vec{j} + (z-1)\vec{k}) = 0 \Rightarrow -2 + 0 + z^2 - z = 0$

$\Rightarrow z^2 - z - 2 = 0 \Rightarrow (z-2)(z+1) = 0 \Rightarrow z = 2 \quad \text{or} \quad -1$

31.

$\vec{V_1} = -200\vec{i}; \quad \vec{V_2} = (-150 \quad \cos 60°)\vec{i}$

$+ (150 \sin 60°)\vec{j}$ (determine $\vec{V_2}$

the way we found $\vec{F}$ in Example 6

in the text).

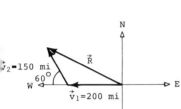

$\vec{R} = \vec{V_1} + \vec{V_2}$

$= -200\vec{i} + (-75\vec{i} + 75\sqrt{3}\,\vec{j})$

$= -275\,\vec{i} + 75\sqrt{3}\,\vec{j}$

35. $(\vec{V} - \alpha\vec{W}) \cdot \vec{W} = \vec{V} \cdot \vec{W} - \alpha(\vec{W} \cdot \vec{W}) = \vec{V} \cdot \vec{W} - \alpha\|\vec{W}\|^2$

(by 14.13). Then $\vec{V} - \alpha\vec{W}$ is perpendicular to $\vec{W}$ if

$\vec{V} \cdot \vec{W} - \alpha\|\vec{W}\|^2 = 0$ or $\alpha = \dfrac{\vec{V} \cdot \vec{W}}{\|\vec{W}\|^2}$ ($\vec{V}$ and $\vec{W}$ nonzero

vectors).

39. $\vec{U} = \|\vec{W}\|\vec{V} + \|\vec{V}\|\vec{W} \Rightarrow \vec{U} \cdot \vec{V} = \|\vec{W}\|(\vec{V} \cdot \vec{V}) + \|\vec{V}\|(\vec{W} \cdot \vec{V})$

$\Rightarrow \vec{U} \cdot \vec{V} = \|\vec{W}\|\|\vec{V}\|^2 + \|\vec{V}\|(\vec{W} \cdot \vec{V}) = \|\vec{V}\|[\|\vec{W}\|\|\vec{V}\| + (\vec{W} \cdot \vec{V})]$.

Similarly, $\vec{U} \cdot \vec{W} = \|\vec{W}\|(\vec{V} \cdot \vec{W}) + \|\vec{V}\|(\vec{W} \cdot \vec{W})$

$= \|\vec{W}\|(\vec{V} \cdot \vec{W}) + \|\vec{V}\|\|\vec{W}\|^2 \Rightarrow \vec{U} \cdot \vec{W} = \|\vec{W}\|[(\vec{V} \cdot \vec{W}) + \|\vec{V}\|\|\vec{W}\|]$.

For θ_V the angle between $\vec{U}$ and $\vec{V}$

and θ_W the angle between $\vec{U}$ and $\vec{W}$,

$\cos \theta_V = \dfrac{\vec{U} \cdot \vec{V}}{\|\vec{U}\|\|\vec{V}\|} = \dfrac{\|\vec{V}\|[\|\vec{W}\|\|\vec{V}\| + (\vec{W} \cdot \vec{V})]}{\|\vec{U}\|\|\vec{V}\|}$

$= \dfrac{\|\vec{W}\|\|\vec{V}\| + (\vec{W} \cdot \vec{V})}{\|\vec{U}\|}$

$\cos \theta_W = \dfrac{\vec{U} \cdot \vec{W}}{\|\vec{U}\|\|\vec{W}\|} = \dfrac{\|\vec{W}\|[(\vec{V} \cdot \vec{W}) + \|\vec{V}\|\|\vec{W}\|]}{\|\vec{U}\|\|\vec{W}\|}$

$= \dfrac{(\vec{V} \cdot \vec{W}) + \|\vec{V}\|\|\vec{W}\|}{\|\vec{U}\|}$

(assuming $\vec{V}$ and $\vec{W}$ are nonzero). Since $\vec{V} \cdot \vec{W}$ = $\vec{W} \cdot \vec{V}$, $\cos \theta_v = \cos \theta_w \Rightarrow \theta_v = \theta_w$ (since $0 \leq \theta_v \leq \pi$ and $0 \leq \theta_w \leq \pi$).

43. Let $\vec{U} = a_1\vec{i} + b_1\vec{j} + c_1\vec{k}$, $\vec{V} = a_2\vec{i} + b_2\vec{j} + c_2\vec{k}$, and $\vec{W} = a_3\vec{i} + b_3\vec{j} + c_3\vec{k}$.

$(\vec{V} + \vec{W}) = (a_2+a_3)\vec{i} + (b_2+b_3)\vec{j} + (c_2+c_3)\vec{k} \Rightarrow$

$$\begin{aligned}
\vec{U} \cdot (\vec{V}+\vec{W}) &= a_1(a_2+a_3) + b_1(b_2+b_3) + c_1(c_2+c_3) \\
&= a_1a_2 + a_1a_3 + b_1b_2 + b_1b_3 + c_1c_2 + c_1c_3 \\
&= (a_1a_2 + b_1b_2 + c_1c_2) + (a_1a_3 + b_1b_3 + c_1c_3) \\
&= (\vec{U} \cdot \vec{V}) + (\vec{U} \cdot \vec{W})
\end{aligned}$$

47. $\vec{V} = a\vec{i} + b\vec{j} + c\vec{k}$

$\vec{V} \cdot \vec{i} = a = 0$

$\vec{V} \cdot \vec{j} = b = 0$

$\vec{V} \cdot \vec{k} = c = 0$

$\Rightarrow \vec{V} = \vec{0}$

Exercise 6, pp. 777-778

3. $\vec{V} \times \vec{W} = \begin{vmatrix} \vec{i} & \vec{j} & \vec{k} \\ 1 & 1 & 0 \\ 1 & -1 & 0 \end{vmatrix} = \begin{vmatrix} 1 & 0 \\ -1 & 0 \end{vmatrix}\vec{i} - \begin{vmatrix} 1 & 0 \\ 1 & 0 \end{vmatrix}\vec{j} + \begin{vmatrix} 1 & 1 \\ 1 & -1 \end{vmatrix}\vec{k}$

$= [0-(0)]\vec{i} - [0-(0)]\vec{j} + [-1-(1)]\vec{k} = -2\vec{k}$

Check: $\vec{V} \cdot (\vec{V}\times\vec{W}) = 1(0) + 1(0) + 0(-2) = 0$

$\vec{W} \cdot (\vec{V}\times\vec{W}) = 1(0) - 1(0) + 0(-2) = 0$

7. $\vec{V} \times \vec{W} = \begin{vmatrix} \vec{i} & \vec{j} & \vec{k} \\ -1 & 8 & 3 \\ 7 & 2 & 0 \end{vmatrix}$

$= \begin{vmatrix} 8 & 3 \\ 2 & 0 \end{vmatrix} \vec{i} - \begin{vmatrix} -1 & 3 \\ 7 & 0 \end{vmatrix} \vec{j} + \begin{vmatrix} -1 & 8 \\ 7 & 2 \end{vmatrix} \vec{k}$

$= (0-6)\vec{i} - (0-21)\vec{j} + (-2-56)\vec{k}$

$= -6\vec{i} + 21\vec{j} - 58\vec{k}$

Check:

$\vec{V} \cdot (\vec{V} \times \vec{W}) = -1(-6) + 8(21) + 3(-58)$

$= 6 + 168 - 174 = 0$

$\vec{W} \cdot (\vec{V} \times \vec{W}) = 7(-6) + 2(21) + 0(-58) = -42 + 42 = 0$

11. $\overrightarrow{PQ} = (2-1)\vec{i} + (1-(-3))\vec{j} + (1-7)\vec{k}$

$= \vec{i} + 4\vec{j} - 6\vec{k}$

$\overrightarrow{PR} = (6-1)\vec{i} + (-1-(-3))\vec{j} + (2-7)\vec{k}$

$= 5\vec{i} + 2\vec{j} - 5\vec{k}$

$\overrightarrow{PQ} \times \overrightarrow{PR} = \begin{vmatrix} \vec{i} & \vec{j} & \vec{k} \\ 1 & 4 & -6 \\ 5 & 2 & -5 \end{vmatrix}$

$= \begin{vmatrix} 4 & -6 \\ 2 & -5 \end{vmatrix} \vec{i} - \begin{vmatrix} 1 & -6 \\ 5 & -5 \end{vmatrix} \vec{j} + \begin{vmatrix} 1 & 4 \\ 5 & 2 \end{vmatrix} \vec{k}$

$= (-20-(-12))\vec{i} - (-5-(-30))\vec{j} + (2-20)\vec{k}$

$= -8\vec{i} - 25\vec{j} - 18\vec{k}$

From (14.28(c)),

Area $= \|\overrightarrow{PQ} \times \overrightarrow{PR}\| = \sqrt{(-8)^2 + (-25)^2 + (-18)^2}$

$$= \sqrt{64 + 625 + 324} = \sqrt{1013}$$

15. $\overrightarrow{PQ} = (5-1)\vec{i} + (-3-1)\vec{j} + (0-(-6))\vec{k}$

$= 4\vec{i} - 4\vec{j} + 6\vec{k}$

$\overrightarrow{PR} = (-2-1)\vec{i} + (4-1)\vec{j} + (1-(-6))\vec{k} = -3\vec{i} + 3\vec{j} + 7\vec{k}$

$\overrightarrow{PQ} \times \overrightarrow{PR} = \begin{vmatrix} \vec{i} & \vec{j} & \vec{k} \\ 4 & -4 & 6 \\ -3 & 3 & 7 \end{vmatrix} = \begin{vmatrix} -4 & 6 \\ 3 & 7 \end{vmatrix}\vec{i} - \begin{vmatrix} 4 & 6 \\ -3 & 7 \end{vmatrix}\vec{j} + \begin{vmatrix} 4 & -4 \\ -3 & 3 \end{vmatrix}\vec{k}$

$= (-28-18)\vec{i} - (28-(-18))\vec{j} + (12-12)\vec{k}$

$= -46\vec{i} - 46\vec{j}$

From (14.28(c)),

Area $= \|\overrightarrow{PQ} \times \overrightarrow{PR}\| = \sqrt{(-46)^2 + (-46)^2 + 0^2}$

$= \sqrt{2116 + 2116 + 0} = \sqrt{4232} = 46\sqrt{2}$

19. $\vec{V} = \overrightarrow{P_1P_2} = 3\vec{i} - 2\vec{k}, \ \vec{W} = \overrightarrow{P_1P_3} = 5\vec{i} - 7\vec{j} + 3\vec{k}$

(Note: $\overrightarrow{P_1P_4} = 8\vec{i} - 7\vec{j} + \vec{k} = \vec{V} + \vec{W}$ is a diagonal.)

$\vec{V} \times \vec{W} = \begin{vmatrix} \vec{i} & \vec{j} & \vec{k} \\ 3 & 0 & -2 \\ 5 & -7 & 3 \end{vmatrix} = (0-14)\vec{i} - [9-(-10)]\vec{j} + (-21-0)\vec{k}$

$= -14\vec{i} - 19\vec{j} - 21\vec{k}$

By (14.28(c)), area $= \|\vec{V} \times \vec{W}\| = \sqrt{196 + 361 + 441} = \sqrt{998}$

23. For $\vec{V} = a_1\vec{i} + b_1\vec{j} + c_1\vec{k}$, $\vec{W} = a_2\vec{i} + b_2\vec{j} + c_2\vec{k}$ and α any scalar,

$\alpha(\vec{V} \times \vec{W}) = \alpha \begin{vmatrix} \vec{i} & \vec{j} & \vec{k} \\ a_1 & b_1 & c_1 \\ a_2 & b_2 & c_2 \end{vmatrix} = \alpha(b_1c_2-b_2c_1)\vec{i} - \alpha(a_1c_2-a_2c_1)\vec{j}$
$+ \alpha(a_1b_2-a_2b_1)\vec{k}$

$$= (\alpha b_1 c_2 - \alpha b_2 c_1)\vec{i} - (\alpha a_1 c_2 - \alpha a_2 c_1)\vec{j} + (\alpha a_1 b_2 - \alpha a_2 b_1)\vec{k}$$

$$(\alpha\vec{V}) \times \vec{W} = \begin{vmatrix} \vec{i} & \vec{j} & \vec{k} \\ \alpha a_1 & \alpha b_1 & \alpha c_1 \\ a_2 & b_2 & c_2 \end{vmatrix} = (\alpha b_1 c_2 - \alpha b_2 c_1)\vec{i} - (\alpha a_1 c_2 - \alpha a_2 c_1)\vec{j}$$
$$+ (\alpha a_1 b_2 - \alpha a_2 b_1)\vec{k}$$

$$\vec{V} \times (\alpha\vec{W}) = \begin{vmatrix} \vec{i} & \vec{j} & \vec{k} \\ a_1 & b_1 & c_1 \\ \alpha a_2 & \alpha b_2 & \alpha c_2 \end{vmatrix} = (\alpha b_1 c_2 - \alpha b_2 c_1)\vec{i} - (\alpha a_1 c_2 - \alpha a_2 c_1)\vec{j}$$
$$+ (\alpha a_1 b_2 - \alpha a_2 b_1)\vec{k}$$

From these results we obtain: $\alpha(\vec{V} \times \vec{W}) = (\alpha\vec{V}) \times \vec{W} = \vec{V} \times (\alpha\vec{W})$.

27. $\vec{U} = a_1\vec{i} + b_1\vec{j} + c_1\vec{k}, \ \vec{V} = a_2\vec{i} + b_2\vec{j} + c_2\vec{k}, \ \vec{W} = a_3\vec{i} + b_3\vec{j} + c_3\vec{k}$

$$\vec{V} \times \vec{W} \quad \begin{vmatrix} \vec{i} & \vec{j} & \vec{k} \\ a_2 & b_2 & c_2 \\ a_3 & b_3 & c_3 \end{vmatrix} = (b_2 c_3 - b_3 c_2)\vec{i} - (a_2 c_3 - a_3 c_2)\vec{j}$$

$$\vec{U} \cdot (\vec{V} \times \vec{W}) = a_1(b_2 c_3 - b_3 c_2) - b_1(a_2 c_3 - a_3 c_2) + c_1(a_2 b_3 - a_3 b_2)$$

$$= a_1 \begin{vmatrix} b_2 & c_2 \\ b_3 & c_3 \end{vmatrix} - b_1 \begin{vmatrix} a_2 & c_2 \\ a_3 & c_3 \end{vmatrix} + c_1 \begin{vmatrix} a_2 & b_2 \\ a_3 & b_3 \end{vmatrix} = \begin{vmatrix} a_1 & b_1 & c_1 \\ a_2 & b_2 & c_2 \\ a_3 & b_3 & c_3 \end{vmatrix}$$

Then, since dot product is commutative,

$$(\vec{U} \times \vec{V}) \cdot \vec{W} = \vec{W} \cdot (\vec{U} \times \vec{V})$$

$$= \begin{vmatrix} a_3 & b_3 & c_3 \\ a_1 & b_1 & c_1 \\ a_2 & b_2 & c_2 \end{vmatrix} \quad \text{(by analogy with the previous result)}$$

From linear algebra, the value of a determinant is multiplied by -1 each time there is an interchange of rows. Since we would need to interchange two sets of rows (first: rows 1 and 2; second: rows 2 and 3), this last determinant is the same as the first determinant in the problem multiplied by $(-1)^2$ (that is, they are identical so $\vec{U} \cdot (\vec{V} \times \vec{W}) = (\vec{U} \times \vec{V}) \cdot \vec{W}$.

Note: We could also expand the determinant for $(\vec{U} \times \vec{V}) \cdot \vec{W}$ to show that it is identical to the value obtained for the determinant for $\vec{U} \cdot (\vec{V} \cdot \vec{W})$.

31.

$$\vec{V} \times \vec{W} = \begin{vmatrix} \vec{i} & \vec{j} & \vec{k} \\ 2 & -6 & -3 \\ 4 & 3 & -1 \end{vmatrix} = [6-(-9)]\vec{i} - [-2-(-12)]\vec{j} + [6-(-24)]\vec{k}$$

$$= 15\vec{i} - 10\vec{j} + 30\vec{k}$$

$$\|\vec{V} \times \vec{W}\| = \sqrt{225 + 100 + 900} = \sqrt{1225} = 35$$

$$\text{Unit vector} = \frac{\vec{V} \times \vec{W}}{\|\vec{V} \times \vec{W}\|} = \frac{15}{35}\vec{i} - \frac{10}{35}\vec{j} + \frac{30}{35}\vec{k}$$

$$= \frac{3}{7}\vec{i} - \frac{2}{7}\vec{j} + \frac{6}{7}\vec{k}$$

Since the direction was not specified,

$$-\left(\frac{3}{7}\vec{i} - \frac{2}{7}\vec{j} + \frac{6}{7}\vec{k}\right) = -\frac{3}{7}\vec{i} + \frac{2}{7}\vec{j} - \frac{6}{7}\vec{k} \text{ is also a unit}$$

vector that works.

35.

Diagonal $\overrightarrow{DB} = \vec{U} - \vec{V}$

Diagonal $\overrightarrow{AC} = \vec{U} + \vec{V}$

Consider $(\vec{U} - \vec{V}) \cdot (\vec{U} + \vec{V})$

$$= \vec{U} \cdot \vec{U} - \vec{V} \cdot \vec{U} + \vec{U} \cdot \vec{V} - \vec{V} \cdot \vec{V}$$

$$= \|\vec{U}\|^2 - \|\vec{V}\|^2 \text{ (by (14.14))}.$$

If the parallelogram is a rhombus, then $\|\vec{U}\| = \|\vec{V}\|$;

thus, $(\vec{U} - \vec{V}) \cdot (\vec{U} + \vec{V}) = 0$, that is, the diagonals are perpendicular. If the diagonals are perpendicular, then $(\vec{U} - \vec{V}) \cdot (\vec{U} + \vec{V}) = 0$ and therefore, $\|\vec{U}\|^2 = \|\vec{V}\|^2$ or $\|\vec{U}\| = \|\vec{V}\|$, that is, the parallelogram is a rhombus.

Exercise 7, pp. 785-787

3. $\vec{r}_1 = 4\vec{i} - \vec{j} + 6\vec{k}, \quad \vec{D} = \vec{i} + \vec{j}$
   $\Rightarrow \vec{r} = (4+t)\vec{i} + (-1+t)\vec{j} + 6\vec{k}$
   $\Rightarrow x = 4 + t, \ y = -1 + t, \ z = 6$
   $\Rightarrow \dfrac{x - 4}{1} = \dfrac{y + 1}{1}, \quad z = 6$

7. $\vec{D} = (2-0)\vec{i} + (3-0)\vec{j} + (1-1)\vec{k} = 2\vec{i} + 3\vec{j}$
   $\vec{r}_1 = \vec{k}$
   $\Rightarrow \vec{r} = (0+2t)\vec{i} + (0+3t)\vec{j} + (1)\vec{k} = 2t\vec{i} + 3t\vec{j} + \vec{k}$
   $\Rightarrow x = 2t, \ y = 3t, \ z = 1$
   $\Rightarrow \dfrac{x}{2} = \dfrac{y}{3}, \quad z = 1$ If the point $(2,3,1)$ had been used
   for $\vec{r}_1$, we would have produced $\dfrac{x-2}{2} = \dfrac{y-3}{3}, \ z = 1.$

11. Set $\vec{r} = \vec{R} \Rightarrow t = -3 + T, \ 1 + 2t = 1 - 4T,$
    $-3 + t = 2 - 7T \Rightarrow$ from the first equation $t = -3 + T$
    $\Rightarrow$ substituting into the other two equations
    $\Rightarrow 1 + 2(-3+T) = 1 - 4T \qquad -3 + (-3+T) = 2 - 7T$
    $\qquad -5 + 2T = 1 - 4T$ and $\qquad -6 + T = 2 - 7T$
    $\qquad \qquad T = 1 \qquad \qquad \qquad \qquad T = 1$

    $\Rightarrow T = 1$ in m and $t = -3 + 1 = -2$ in ℓ
    $\Rightarrow$ point of intersection $(-2,-3,-5).$

    Line ℓ is parallel to $\vec{V} = \vec{i} + 2\vec{j} + \vec{k}, \ $ m is
    parallel to $\vec{W} = \vec{i} - 4\vec{j} - 7\vec{k}.$ From (14.18),

$$\cos\theta = \frac{\vec{V} \cdot \vec{W}}{\|\vec{V}\|\|\vec{W}\|} = \frac{1(1) + 2(-4) + 1(-7)}{\sqrt{1 + 4 + 1}\sqrt{1 + 16 + 49}}$$

$$= \frac{-14}{\sqrt{6}\sqrt{66}} = \frac{-7}{3\sqrt{11}}$$

15. Given $\vec{a} = 2\vec{i} + 4\vec{j} - 2\vec{k}$ and $\vec{b} = -3\vec{i} - 2\vec{j} + \vec{k}$.

   A vector perpendicular to both $\vec{a}$ and $\vec{b}$ is

$$\vec{a} \times \vec{b} \begin{vmatrix} \vec{i} & \vec{j} & \vec{k} \\ 2 & 4 & -2 \\ -3 & -2 & 1 \end{vmatrix} = \begin{vmatrix} 4 & -2 \\ -2 & 1 \end{vmatrix}\vec{i} - \begin{vmatrix} 2 & -2 \\ -3 & 1 \end{vmatrix}\vec{j} + \begin{vmatrix} 2 & 4 \\ -3 & -2 \end{vmatrix}\vec{k}$$

$$= 0\vec{i} + 4\vec{j} + 8\vec{k}$$

   Line parallel to this vector, through $P(1,2,-1)$

   $\Rightarrow x = 1$, $\dfrac{y - 2}{4} = \dfrac{z + 1}{8}$

19. ℓ parallel to $\vec{V} = \vec{i} - \vec{j} + 6\vec{k}$, m parallel to
   $\vec{W} = \vec{i} - \vec{j} - 2\vec{k}$; $\vec{V}$, $\vec{W}$ not parallel $\Rightarrow \ell$, m not
   parallel. Set $\vec{r} = \vec{R} \Rightarrow 4 + t = 4 + T$, $3 - t = 3 - T$,
   $6t = 2 - 2T \Rightarrow$ from the first two equations, $t = T$
   $\Rightarrow$ substituting in the third equation $\Rightarrow 6(T) = 2 - 2T$
   or $T = \dfrac{1}{4}$ (and $t = \dfrac{1}{4}$) $\Rightarrow$ point of intersection
   $(\dfrac{17}{4}, \dfrac{11}{4}, \dfrac{3}{2})$.

23. ℓ parallel to $\vec{V} = 2\vec{i} + 3\vec{j} + 4\vec{k}$, m parallel to
   $\vec{W} = -4\vec{i} - 6\vec{j} - 8\vec{k}$; $\vec{W} = -2\vec{V} \Rightarrow \ell$, m are parallel.

27. ℓ parallel to $\vec{V} = 6\vec{i} + 3\vec{j} + 7\vec{k}$, m parallel to
   $\vec{W} = 6\vec{i} + 3\vec{j} + 7\vec{k}$; $\vec{V} = \vec{W} \Rightarrow \ell$ and m are parallel.

31. ℓ is parallel to $\vec{V} = a_1\vec{i} + a_2\vec{j} + a_3\vec{k}$, m is
   parallel to $\vec{W} = b_1\vec{i} + b_2\vec{j} + b_3\vec{k}$. If $\alpha = \dfrac{a_1}{b_1} = \dfrac{a_2}{b_2}$

$= \dfrac{a_3}{b_3}$, then $\vec{V} = \alpha\vec{W} \Rightarrow \ell$, m are parallel.

35. See Example 10.

$\vec{U} = \vec{i} + \vec{j} + \vec{k} \Rightarrow \dfrac{\vec{a}}{\|\vec{a}\|} = \dfrac{1}{\sqrt{3}}(\vec{i} + \vec{j} + \vec{k})$ is a unit

vector parallel to the axis ℓ of rotation $\Rightarrow \omega = 30$

$\Rightarrow \vec{\omega} = \pm 30 \dfrac{1}{\sqrt{3}}(\vec{i} + \vec{j} + \vec{k}) \Rightarrow \vec{\omega} = \pm 10\sqrt{3}(\vec{i} + \vec{j} + \vec{k}).$

Position vector of particle is $\vec{r} = -\vec{i} + 2\vec{j} + 3\vec{k}.$

By (14.36),

$\vec{V} = \vec{\omega} \times \vec{r} = \pm 10\sqrt{3} \begin{vmatrix} \vec{i} & \vec{j} & \vec{k} \\ 1 & 1 & 1 \\ -1 & 2 & 3 \end{vmatrix}$

$= \pm 10\sqrt{3}(\vec{i} - 4\vec{j} + 3\vec{k})$

$\Rightarrow$ speed $= \|\vec{V}\| = 10\sqrt{3} \sqrt{1 + 16 + 9} = 10\sqrt{3}\sqrt{26}$

$= 10\sqrt{78}$ m/sec.

Exercise 8, pp. 791-793

3. Parallel xz-plane $\Rightarrow$ y = k, k = constant
   containing the point (1,-2,3) $\Rightarrow$ y = -2

7. $P_1 = (0,1,5)$, $\vec{N} = 2\vec{i} + \vec{j} + 3\vec{k} \Rightarrow$
   $2(x-0) + 1(y-1) + 3(z-5) = 0 \Rightarrow 2x + y + 3z = 16$

11. $P_1 = (10,3,-4)$; parallel to x - y + 3z = 5
    $\Rightarrow \vec{N} = \vec{i} - \vec{j} + 3\vec{k} \Rightarrow 1(x-10) - 1(y-3) + 3[z-(-4)] = 0$
    $\Rightarrow$ x - y + 3z = -5

15. $P_1 = (0,1,-2)$; perpendicular to $\dfrac{x-1}{2} = \dfrac{y+3}{3}$
    $= \dfrac{z-2}{2} \Rightarrow \vec{N} = 2\vec{i} + 3\vec{j} + 2\vec{k} \Rightarrow 2(x-0) + 3(y-1)$
    $+ 2[z-(-2)] = 0 \Rightarrow 2x + 3y + 2z = -1$

19. Perpendicular to $2x - y + z = 6 \Rightarrow$ parallel to
$\vec{N} = 2\vec{i} - \vec{j} + \vec{k} \Rightarrow$ through the point $P_1 = (1,2,-1)$
$\Rightarrow$ line: $x = 1 + 2t$, $y = 2 - t$, $z = -1 + t$.

23. Plane: $2x + 3y + z = 5$, line: $x = 3 + t$,
$y = -4 + 2t$, $z = 1 + 2t \Rightarrow 2(3+t) + 3(-4+2t) + (1+2t)$
$= 5 \Rightarrow 6 + 2t - 12 + 6t + 1 + 2t = 5 \Rightarrow 10t = 10$
$\Rightarrow t = 1 \Rightarrow$ point of intersection: $(4,-2,3)$.

For Problems 25-30, see Example 2.

27. $\vec{V} = \overrightarrow{P_1P_2} = 2\vec{i} + \vec{k}$, $\vec{W} = \overrightarrow{P_1P_3} = 3\vec{i} - 3\vec{j} - 2\vec{k}$

$\vec{N} = \vec{V} \times \vec{W} = \begin{vmatrix} \vec{i} & \vec{j} & \vec{k} \\ 2 & 0 & 1 \\ 3 & -3 & -2 \end{vmatrix} = 3\vec{i} + 7\vec{j} - 6\vec{k}$

$P_1 = (1,2,1) \Rightarrow$ plane: $3(x-1) + 7(y-2) - 6(z-1) = 0$
$\Rightarrow 3x + 7y - 6z = 11$

31. $\vec{N_1} = 2\vec{i} - \vec{j} + \vec{k}$, $\vec{N_2} = \vec{i} + \vec{j} + \vec{k} \Rightarrow$ planes not
parallel $\Rightarrow$ planes intersect. From (14.40),

$$\cos \theta = \frac{|\vec{N_1} \cdot \vec{N_2}|}{\|\vec{N_1}\|\|\vec{N_2}\|} = \frac{|2(1) - 1(1) + 1(1)|}{\sqrt{4 + 1 + 1}\sqrt{1 + 1 + 1}} = \frac{2}{3\sqrt{2}} = \frac{\sqrt{2}}{3}$$

35. $\vec{N_1} = 2\vec{i} - \vec{j} + \vec{k}$, $\vec{N_2} = 4\vec{i} - \vec{j} + 6\vec{k} \Rightarrow$ planes not
parallel $\Rightarrow$ planes intersect. From (14.40),

$$\cos \theta = \frac{|\vec{N_1} \cdot \vec{N_2}|}{\|\vec{N_1}\|\|\vec{N_2}\|} = \frac{|2(4) - 1(-1) + 1(6)|}{\sqrt{4 + 1 + 1}\sqrt{16 + 1 + 36}} = \frac{15}{\sqrt{6}\sqrt{53}}$$

$$= \frac{15}{\sqrt{318}} = \frac{5\sqrt{3}}{\sqrt{106}}$$

39. From (14.41) for $2x - y + z = 1$, $P_0 = (1,2,-1)$

$$\Rightarrow d = \frac{|2(1) - (2) + (-1) - 1|}{\sqrt{4 + 1 + 1}} = \frac{2}{\sqrt{6}} = \sqrt{\frac{2}{3}}$$

Exercise 9, pp. 803-805

3. $x^2 + 2y^2 + z^2 = 4$. In standard form, $\frac{x^2}{4} + \frac{y^2}{2} + \frac{z^2}{4} = 1$.

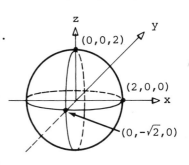

Ellipsoid with intercepts at
$(\pm2,0,0)$, $(0,\pm\sqrt{2},0)$, $(0,0,\pm2)$.
Since we have a special case
of equation (14.42) in which
$a = c > b$, the surface is
called an oblate spheroid.
Sections parallel to the
xz-plane (between the
y-intercepts) are circles.
Note that the usual xy
perspective has been rotated.

7. $x = 4y^2$. Parabolic cylinder,
generated by a line parallel
to the z-axis moving along
the parabola $x = 4y^2$.

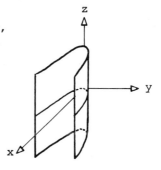

11. $y^2 - x^2 = 4$. In standard

form $\frac{y^2}{4} - \frac{x^2}{4} = 1$.
Hyperbolic cylinder,
generated by a line
parallel to the z-axis
moving along the hyperbola

$\frac{y^2}{4} - \frac{x^2}{4} = 1$.

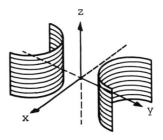

15. $4y^2 - x^2 = 1$. Hyperbolic cylinder, generated by a line parallel to the z-axis moving along the hyperbola $4y^2 - x^2 = 1$.

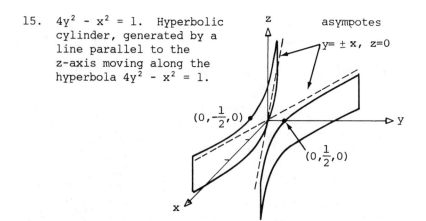

19. $y = 4x^2 + 9z^2$. Elliptic paraboloid, with vertex at the origin and symmetric about the positive y-axis. Sections parallel to the xz-plane, for $y > 0$, are ellipses.

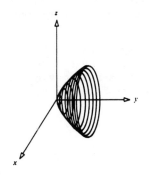

23. Since the z-variable is missing, z is unrestricted, and the graph may be generated by a line moving along the curve $xy = 1$, while remaining parallel to the z-axis. A surface generated in this way is termed a cylinder. This graph is a quadric surface as its equation fits the general form $Ax^2 + By^2 + Cz^2 + Dxy + Exz + Fyz + Gx + Hy + Iz + J = 0$ with $A = B = C = E = F = G = H = I = 0$, $D = 1$, $J = -1$.

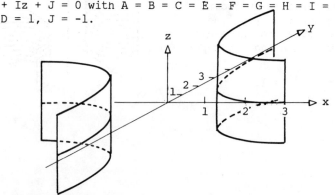

27. $3x^2 + 2y^2 - (z-2)^2 + 1 = 0$

   $3x^2 + 2y^2 - (z-2)^2 = -1$

   Hyperboloid of two sheets, opens around the z-axis
   => figure H.

31. (a) Hyperbolic paraboloid: Figure L
   (b) Elliptic paraboloid: Figure O
   (c) Hyperboloid of one sheet: Figure K
   (d) Ellipsoid: Figure M
   (e) Parabolic cylinder: Figure N

Historical Exercises, pp. 807-808

3. $Z = a + bi$, $\overline{Z} = a - bi$, $W = c + di$, $\overline{W} = c - di$

   (a) $Z \diamond W = Z\overline{W} = (a+bi)(c-di) = ac - adi + bci - bdi^2$

   $$(\text{use } i^2 = -1)$$

   $$= (ac+bd) + (bc-ad)i, \quad \text{a complex number}$$

   (b)(i) $W \diamond Z = W\overline{Z} = (c+di)(a-bi)$

   $$= ca - cbi + dai - dbi^2 \quad (\text{use } i^2 = -1)$$

   $$= (ac+bd) + (ad-bc)i = (ac+bd) - (bc-ad)i$$

   $$= \overline{Z \diamond W}, \quad \text{but not necessarily } Z \diamond W$$

   (ii) Let $R = e + fi$, $Z = a + bi$, $W = c + di$

   $$R \diamond (Z+W) = R(\overline{Z+W}) = R[\overline{(a+bi) + (c+di)}]$$

   $$= R[\overline{(a+c) + (b+d)i}] = R[(a+c) - (b+d)i]$$

   $$= R[(a-bi) + (c-di)] = R(\overline{Z}+\overline{W})$$

   $$= R\overline{Z} + R\overline{W} = R \diamond Z + R \diamond W$$

   (iii) $\alpha(Z \diamond W) = \alpha(Z\overline{W}) = \alpha Z\overline{W} = (\alpha Z)\overline{W} = (\alpha Z) \diamond W$

   (iv) $0 \diamond Z = (0+0i)(a-bi) = 0$

   (v) $Z \diamond Z = Z\overline{Z} = (a+bi)(a-bi) = a^2 + b^2$

   $$= (\text{modulus (length) of } Z)^2$$

   Therefore, every part of (14.13) is satisfied except
   the commutativity, part (a).

3. (a) From (14.18), $\cos \theta = \dfrac{\vec{V} \cdot \vec{W}}{\|\vec{V}\| \|\vec{W}\|}$; therefore,

$\sin^2 \theta = 1 - \cos^2 \theta = 1 - (\dfrac{\vec{V} \cdot \vec{W}}{\|\vec{V}\| \|\vec{W}\|})^2$

$= \dfrac{\|\vec{V}\|^2 \|\vec{W}\|^2 - (\vec{V} \cdot \vec{W})^2}{\|\vec{V}\|^2 \|\vec{W}\|^2}$

(b) $\vec{V}$, $\vec{W}$ parallel means $\theta = 0$ or π, that is, $\sin \theta = 0$. From part (a), the only time we can get $\sin \theta = 0$ is when $\|\vec{V}\|^2 \|\vec{W}\|^2 - (\vec{V} \cdot \vec{W})^2 = 0$ or $\|\vec{V}\| \|\vec{W}\| = |\vec{V} \cdot \vec{W}|$. [This also gives the condition for equality in the Cauchy-Schwarz inequality (14.20).]

7. ℓ is parallel to $\vec{V} = \vec{i} + 3\vec{j} + \vec{k}$, m is parallel to $\vec{W} = 2\vec{i} + 3\vec{j} + \vec{k}$

$\vec{N} = \vec{V} \times \vec{W} = \begin{vmatrix} \vec{i} & \vec{j} & \vec{k} \\ 1 & 3 & 1 \\ 2 & 3 & 1 \end{vmatrix} = \vec{j} - 3\vec{k}$

is a normal to the required plane. We need only a point in the plane. Write m: x = -3 + 2T, y = 3 + 3T, z = T $\Rightarrow$ set ℓ = m $\Rightarrow$ t + 1 = -3 + 2T, 3t = 3 + 3T, t -1 = T $\Rightarrow$ substitute the third equation into the other two equations $\Rightarrow$

t + 1 = -3 + 2(t-1)	3t = 3 + 3(t-1)	
t + 1 = -5 + 2t and	3t = 3t	$\Rightarrow$
6 = t	0 = 0	

t = 6 in ℓ
and
T = 6 - 1
= 5 in m

$\Rightarrow$ point of intersection: (7,18,5) $\Rightarrow$ from (14.38)
$\Rightarrow$ plane: 0(x-7) + 1(y-18) - 3(z-5) = 0 $\Rightarrow$ y - 3z = 3.

11. (a) From (14.39), $\vec{N} = A\vec{i} + B\vec{j} + C\vec{k}$ is perpendicular
to the plane. From (14.32), the line through
$P_0 = (x_0, y_0, z_0)$ parallel to $\vec{N}$ is $x = x_0 + At$,
$y = y_0 + Bt$, $Z = z_0 + Ct$.

(b) To find $P(x,y,z)$, the point of intersection
of the line and the plane, substitute the line
equations into the plane:

$A(x_0 + At) + B(y_0 + Bt) + C(z_0 + Ct) = D$

$Ax_0 + By_0 + Cz_0 + t(A^2 + B^2 + C^2) = D$

$t = \dfrac{-(Ax_0 + By_0 + Cz_0) + D}{A^2 + B^2 + C^2}$ $\Rightarrow$ then substitute

this into the line equations, $x = x_0 + At$,
$y = y_0 + Bt$, $Z = z_0 + Ct$.

(c) Since P lies in the plane and P_0 lies on
the line through P and P_0 that is
perpendicular to the plane, then d is the
distance from P_0 to P.

$d = \sqrt{(x-x_0)^2 + (y-y_0)^2 + (z-z_0)^2}$

$= \sqrt{A^2 t^2 + B^2 t^2 + C^2 t^2} = |t| \sqrt{A^2 + B^2 + C^2}$

$= \dfrac{|-(Ax_0 + By_0 + Cz_0) + D|}{A^2 + B^2 + C^2} \sqrt{A^2 + B^2 + C^2}$

$= \dfrac{|-(Ax_0 + By_0 + Cz_0) + D|}{\sqrt{A^2 + B^2 + C^2}}$

or

$d = \dfrac{|Ax_0 + By_0 + Cz_0 - D|}{\sqrt{A^2 + B^2 + C^2}}$

15.

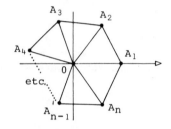

n-sided
regular
polygon

All central angles $= \dfrac{2\pi}{n}$

All angles formed by successive sides of the polygon $= 2(\dfrac{\pi - 2\pi/n}{2})$

$= \pi - \dfrac{2\pi}{n}$

An n-sided regular polygon is made up of n successive equal lines, each at an angle $\pi - \dfrac{2\pi}{n}$ from the previous line, moving (as in this case) in a counterclockwise fashion. Now, take all vectors $\overrightarrow{OA_1}, \ldots, \overrightarrow{OA_n}$

and set them end to end so that the initial point (O) coincides with the terminal side of the previous vector (as in the illustration below). Since all vectors $\overrightarrow{OA_n}$ are of equal length and each is at an angle of $\pi - \dfrac{2\pi}{n}$ from each other, we will create an n-sided regular polygon with the n vectors $\overrightarrow{OA_n}$ forming the n-sides. Since this is a *closed* figure, the vectors cancel out, that is,

$\displaystyle\sum_{i=1}^{n} OA_i = \vec{0}.$

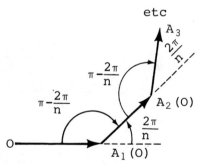

19. $\vec{U} = a_1\vec{i} + b_1\vec{j}$, $\vec{V} = a_2\vec{i} + b_2\vec{j}$; $\vec{U},\vec{V}$ nonparallel

$\Rightarrow \dfrac{a_1}{a_2} \neq \dfrac{b_1}{b_2} \Rightarrow a_1b_2 - a_2b_1 \neq 0$. For $\vec{W} = W_1\vec{i} + W_2\vec{j}$,

solve $\vec{W} = s\vec{U} + t\vec{V}$ for s and t.

$sa_1 + ta_2 = W_1 \qquad -sa_1b_1 - ta_2b_1 = -W_1b_1$

$sb_1 + sb_2 = W_2 \overset{\Rightarrow}{\quad} sa_1b_1 + ta_1b_2 = W_2a_1$

$\Rightarrow \quad t = \dfrac{-W_1b_1 + W_2a_1}{a_1b_2 - a_2b_1}$ Also, $\begin{array}{l} sa_1b_2 + ta_2b_2 = W_1b_2 \\ -sa_2b_1 - ta_2b_2 = -W_2a_2 \end{array}$

$\Rightarrow \quad s = \dfrac{W_1b_2 - W_2a_2}{a_1b_2 - a_2b_1}$

All vectors in the plane can be represented by a unique linear combination of two nonparallel vectors.

23. Substitute the four given points into

$x^2 + y^2 + z^2 + ax + by + cz = d$ and solve for

a,b,c, and d.

#1 $9 + 3a = d$
#2 $1 + c = d$
#3 $11 - a - 3b + c = d$
#4 $5 + 2a + c = d$

#1 and #2 $\Rightarrow 9 + 3a = 1 + c \Rightarrow 3a - c = -8$;

#2 and #4 $\Rightarrow 1 + c = 5 + 2a + c \Rightarrow -4 = 2a \Rightarrow a = -2$;

Therefore, $3(-2) - c = -8 \Rightarrow c = 2$; and from #2,

$1 + 2 = d \Rightarrow d = 3$; then in #3, $11 - (-2) - 3b + 2 = 3$

$\Rightarrow b = 4$. Sphere: $x^2 + y^2 + z^2 - 2x + 4y + 2z = 3$.

27. $\vec{U} = \overrightarrow{AB} = \vec{i} + 4\vec{k}$, $\vec{V} = \overrightarrow{AC} = 2\vec{i} - \vec{j} + \vec{k}$,

$\vec{W} = \overrightarrow{AD} = 3\vec{i} + 4\vec{j} + 8\vec{k}$

$\vec{V} \times \vec{W} = \begin{vmatrix} \vec{i} & \vec{j} & \vec{k} \\ 2 & -1 & 1 \\ 3 & 4 & 8 \end{vmatrix} = -12\vec{i} - 13\vec{j} + 11\vec{k}$

From (14.29), volume of parallelepiped

$= |\vec{U} \cdot (\vec{V} \times \vec{W})|$; volume $= |-12 + 44| = 32$.

31. $(2x + y - z = 6) + (x - y + 3z = 4) \Rightarrow 3x + 2z = 10$

$\Rightarrow x = -\dfrac{2}{3} z + \dfrac{10}{3}$

$(2x + y - z = 6) - 2(x - y + 3z = 4) \Rightarrow 3y - 7z = -2$

$\Rightarrow y = \dfrac{7}{3} z - \dfrac{2}{3}$

Choose $z = 3t \Rightarrow x = -2t + \dfrac{10}{3}$, $y = 7t - \dfrac{2}{3}$.

(These are the parametric equations of the line of intersection.)

Symmetric equations: $\dfrac{x - \dfrac{10}{3}}{-2} = \dfrac{y + \dfrac{2}{3}}{7} = \dfrac{z}{3}$

35. Since $\|\vec{U}\| > 0$, $\|\vec{V}\| > 0$ (we assume $\vec{U} \neq \vec{0}$, $\vec{V} \neq \vec{0}$), $\vec{W} = \|\vec{V}\|\vec{U} + \|\vec{U}\|\vec{V}$ is a vector positioned between $\vec{U}$ and $\vec{V}$. Let α be the angle between $\vec{U}$ and $\vec{W}$ and β be the angle between $\vec{W}$ and $\vec{V}$. By (14.18),

$\cos \alpha = \dfrac{\vec{U} \cdot \vec{W}}{\|\vec{U}\| \|\vec{W}\|} = \dfrac{\|\vec{V}\| (\vec{U} \cdot \vec{U}) + \|\vec{U}\| (\vec{U} \cdot \vec{V})}{\|\vec{U}\| \|\vec{W}\|}$

(use $\vec{U} \cdot \vec{U} = \|\vec{U}\|^2$)

$= \dfrac{\|\vec{V}\| \|\vec{U}\| + (\vec{U} \cdot \vec{V})}{\|\vec{W}\|}$

$\cos \beta = \dfrac{\vec{W} \cdot \vec{V}}{\|\vec{W}\| \|\vec{V}\|} = \dfrac{\|\vec{V}\| (\vec{U} \cdot \vec{V}) + \|\vec{U}\| (\vec{V} \cdot \vec{V})}{\|\vec{W}\| \|\vec{V}\|}$

(use $\vec{V} \cdot \vec{V} = \|\vec{V}\|^2$)

$= \dfrac{(\vec{U} \cdot \vec{V}) + \|\vec{U}\| \|\vec{V}\|}{\|\vec{W}\|}$

$\Rightarrow \cos \alpha = \cos \beta$ ($0 \leq \alpha$, $\beta \leq \pi$) $\Rightarrow \alpha = \beta$
$\Rightarrow \vec{W}$ bisects the angle between $\vec{U}$ and $\vec{V}$.

39. $(\vec{r} - \vec{b}) \cdot (\vec{r} + \vec{b}) = 0 \Rightarrow \vec{r} \cdot \vec{r} - \vec{r} \cdot \vec{b} + \vec{b} \cdot \vec{r}$
$- \vec{b} \cdot \vec{b} = 0 \Rightarrow \|\vec{r}\|^2 - \|\vec{b}\|^2 = 0 \Rightarrow \|\vec{r}\|^2 = \|\vec{b}\|^2$

$\Rightarrow x^2 + y^2 + z^2 = \|\vec{b}\|^2 \Rightarrow$ sphere, center at $(0,0,0)$, radius $= \|\vec{b}\|$.

$(\vec{r} - \vec{r_0} - \vec{b}) \cdot (\vec{r} - \vec{r_0} + \vec{b}) = 0$

$\Rightarrow (\vec{r} - \vec{r_0}) \cdot (\vec{r} - \vec{r_0}) - (\vec{r} - \vec{r_0}) \cdot \vec{b} + (\vec{r} - \vec{r_0}) \cdot \vec{b}$

$- \vec{b} \cdot \vec{b} = 0 \Rightarrow \|\vec{r} - \vec{r_0}\|^2 - \|\vec{b}\|^2 = 0 \Rightarrow \|\vec{r} - \vec{r_0}\|^2$

$= \|\vec{b}\|^2 \Rightarrow (x-x_0)^2 + (y-y_0)^2 + (z-z_0)^2 = \|\vec{b}\|^2$

$\Rightarrow$ sphere, center at (x_0, y_0, z_0), radius $= \|\vec{b}\|$.

43. Plane is parallel to $\vec{r} = 2\vec{i} + t(-\vec{i} + \vec{j} + 2\vec{k})$, that is, parallel to the vector $\vec{V} = -\vec{i} + \vec{j} + 2\vec{k}$. Since the plane contains A, B, it is parallel to $\overrightarrow{AB} = -\vec{i} - 2\vec{j} + 2\vec{k}$. Therefore, its normal vector is

$$\vec{N} = \vec{V} \times \overrightarrow{AB} = \begin{vmatrix} \vec{i} & \vec{j} & \vec{k} \\ -1 & 1 & 2 \\ -1 & -2 & 2 \end{vmatrix} = 6\vec{i} + 3\vec{k}$$

Equation of plane: $6(x-2) + 0(y-2) + 3[z-(-1)] = 0$
$\Rightarrow 6x + 3z = 9 \Rightarrow 2x + z = 3$

47. $\sin^2\theta = 1 - \cos^2\theta = 1 - (\dfrac{\vec{U} \cdot \vec{V}}{\|\vec{U}\| \|\vec{V}\|})^2 = \dfrac{\|\vec{U}\|^2 \|\vec{V}\|^2 - (\vec{U} \cdot \vec{V})^2}{\|\vec{U}\|^2 \|\vec{V}\|^2}$

(same result as in Problem 3(a))

$= \dfrac{\|\vec{U} \times \vec{V}\|^2}{\|\vec{U}\|^2 \|\vec{V}\|^2}$ (use 14.27(e))

(This same result can be obtained by squaring both sides of (14.28b).) Now, use (14.25) for $\vec{U} \times \vec{V}$

$= \dfrac{(a_2 b_3 - a_3 b_2)^2 + (a_1 b_3 - a_3 b_1)^2 + (a_1 b_2 - a_2 b_1)^2}{\|\vec{U}\|^2 \|\vec{V}\|^2}$

Chapter Fifteen

<u>Exercise 1</u>, 823-825

3. $\vec{r}(t) = t\vec{i} + t\vec{j}$; $x = t$, $y = t \Rightarrow y = x$

7. $\vec{r}(t) = (\cos t)\vec{i} - (\sin t)\vec{j}$, $0 \leq t \leq \frac{\pi}{2}$; $x = \cos t$,
   $y = -\sin t \Rightarrow x^2 + y^2 = \cos^2 t + \sin^2 t = 1$; $\vec{r}(0) = \vec{i}$,
   $\vec{r}(\frac{\pi}{2}) = -\vec{j}$

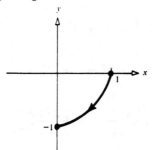

11. $\vec{r}(t) = (e^t \cos t)\vec{i} + (e^t \sin t)\vec{j} + t\vec{k}$
    $\vec{r}\,'(t) = (e^t \cos t - e^t \sin t)\vec{i} + (e^t \sin t + e^t \cos t)\vec{j} + \vec{k}$
    $\vec{r}\,''(t) = (-2e^t \sin t)\vec{i} + (2e^t \cos t)\vec{j}$

15. $\vec{r}(t) = t\vec{i} + t^2\vec{j} \Rightarrow x = t$, $y = t^2$

    $\vec{r}\,'(t) = \vec{i} + 2t\vec{j}$

    $\vec{r}(0) = \vec{0}$

    $\vec{r}\,'(0) = \vec{i}$

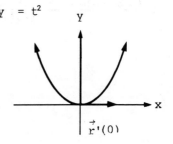

19. $\vec{r}(t) = 3 \sin t \vec{i} - 3 \cos t \vec{j}$

$\Rightarrow x = 3 \sin t, \ y = -3 \cos t$

$\Rightarrow x^2 + y^2 = 9 \sin^2 t + 9 \cos^2 t = 9(\sin^2 t + \cos^2 t)$

$\Rightarrow x^2 + y^2 = 9$ (circle of radius 3)

$\vec{r}'(t) = 3 \cos t \vec{i} + 3 \sin t \vec{j}$

$\vec{r}(0) = -3\vec{j}$

$\vec{r}'(0) = 3\vec{i}$

23. $\vec{r}(t) = (1-3t)\vec{i} + 2t\vec{j} - (5+t)\vec{k} \Rightarrow \vec{r}(0) = \vec{i} - 5\vec{k}$

$\vec{r}'(t) = -3\vec{i} + 2\vec{j} - \vec{k} \Rightarrow \vec{r}'(0) = -3\vec{i} + 2\vec{j} - \vec{k}$

$\vec{R}(u) = \vec{r}(0) + u\vec{r}'(0) = (1-3u)\vec{i} + 2u\vec{j} + (-5-u)\vec{k}$

27. $\vec{r}(t) = (2 \cos t)\vec{i} + \vec{j} + (2 \sin t)\vec{k} \Rightarrow \vec{r}(0) = 2\vec{i} + \vec{j}$

$\vec{r}'(t) = (-2 \sin t)\vec{i} + (2 \cos t)\vec{k} \Rightarrow \vec{r}'(0) = 2\vec{k}$

$\vec{R}(u) = \vec{r}(0) + u\vec{r}'(0) = 2\vec{i} + \vec{j} + 2u\vec{k}$

31. $\vec{f}(t) = 2t\vec{i} + t^2\vec{j} - 5\vec{k}, \quad \vec{g}(t) = t^2\vec{i} + 2t\vec{j} + \vec{k}$

$\vec{f}(t) \cdot \vec{g}(t) = 2t^3 + 2t^3 - 5 = 4t^3 - 5$

$\Rightarrow [\vec{f}(t) \cdot \vec{g}(t)]' = 12t^2$

$[\vec{f}(t) \times \vec{g}(t)]' = \vec{f}'(t) \times \vec{g}(t) + \vec{f}(t) \times \vec{g}'(t)$

$$= \begin{vmatrix} \vec{i} & \vec{j} & \vec{k} \\ 2 & 2t & 0 \\ t^2 & 2t & 1 \end{vmatrix} + \begin{vmatrix} \vec{i} & \vec{j} & \vec{k} \\ 2t & t^2 & -5 \\ 2t & 2 & 0 \end{vmatrix}$$

$$= (2t\vec{i} - 2\vec{j} + (4t-2t^3)\vec{k})$$
$$+ [10\vec{i} - 10t\vec{j} + (4t-2t^3)\vec{k}]$$
$$= (2t+10)\vec{i} + (-2-10t)\vec{j} + (8t-4t^3)\vec{k}$$

35. $\vec{f}(t) = e^{2t}\vec{i} + e^{-2t}\vec{j} + t\vec{k}, \quad \vec{g}(t) = e^{-t}\vec{i} + e^{-2t}\vec{j} - t\vec{k}$

$[\vec{f}(t) \cdot \vec{g}(t)]' = (e^t + e^{-4t} - t^2)' = e^t - 4e^{-4t} - 2t$

$$\vec{f}(t) \times \vec{g}(t) = \begin{vmatrix} \vec{i} & \vec{j} & \vec{k} \\ e^{2t} & e^{-2t} & t \\ e^{-t} & e^{-2t} & -t \end{vmatrix}$$

$$= -2te^{-2t}\vec{i} + (te^{2t} + te^{-t})\vec{j} + (1-e^{-3t})\vec{k}$$

$[\vec{f}(t) \times \vec{g}(t)]' = (-2e^{-2t} + 4te^{-2t})\vec{i}$
$$+ (e^{2t} + 2te^{2t} + e^{-t} - te^{-t})\vec{j}$$
$$+ 3e^{-3t}\vec{k}$$

39. $\vec{r}(t) = t^2\vec{i} + (t^2-1)\vec{j} - t\vec{k}$

$\vec{r}'(t) = 2t\vec{i} + 2t\vec{j} - \vec{k}$

$\vec{r}(t), \vec{r}'(t)$ orthogonal $\Rightarrow \vec{r}(t) \cdot \vec{r}'(t)$

$= 2t^3 + 2t^3 - 2t + t = 0 \Rightarrow 4t^3 - t = 0$

$\Rightarrow t(2t-1)(2t+1) = 0 \Rightarrow t = 0, 1/2, -1/2$

$\Rightarrow$ substitute the values into $\vec{r}(t) \Rightarrow (0,-1,0)$,

$(\frac{1}{4}, -\frac{3}{4}, -\frac{1}{2})$, $(\frac{1}{4}, -\frac{3}{4}, \frac{1}{2})$

43. $\vec{r}_1(t) = t^2\vec{i} + (\sin\pi t)\vec{j} + \vec{k}$

$\Rightarrow \vec{r}_1'(t) = 2t\vec{i} + (\pi\cos\pi t)\vec{j}$

$\vec{r}_2(T) = \vec{i} + T\vec{j} + (1+T)\vec{k}$

$\Rightarrow \vec{r}_2'(T) = \vec{j} + \vec{k}$

$(1,0,1)$ point of intersection of $\vec{r}_1(t)$ and $\vec{r}_2(T)$

$\Rightarrow t = 1, T = 0; \quad \vec{r}_1'(1) = 2\vec{i} - \pi\vec{j}, \vec{r}_2'(0) = \vec{j} + \vec{k};$

$\cos\theta = \dfrac{\vec{r}_1'(1) \cdot \vec{r}_2'(0)}{\|\vec{r}_1'(1)\|\|\vec{r}_2'(0)\|} = \dfrac{-\pi}{\sqrt{4 + \pi^2}\sqrt{1 + 1}} = \dfrac{-\pi}{\sqrt{2}\sqrt{4 + \pi^2}}$

$\Rightarrow \theta = \cos^{-1}(\dfrac{-\pi}{\sqrt{2}\sqrt{4 + \pi^2}})$

47. By (14.27c), $\vec{V} \times \vec{W} = -(\vec{W} \times \vec{V}) \Rightarrow [\vec{f}(t) \times \vec{g}(t)]'$

$= \{-[\vec{g}(t) \times \vec{f}(t)]\}' = -[\vec{g}(t) \times \vec{f}(t)]'$

<u>Exercise 2</u>, pp. 830-832

3. $\vec{r}(t) = t\vec{i} + e^t\vec{j}$

$\Rightarrow x = t, \ y = e^t \Rightarrow y = e^x$

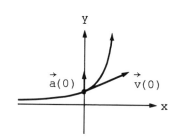

$\vec{r}(t) = \vec{r}'(t) = \vec{i} + e^t\vec{j}$

$\vec{a}(t) = \vec{r}''(t) = e^t\vec{j}$

$\vec{v}(0) = \vec{i} + \vec{j}$

$\vec{a}(0) = \vec{j}$

7. $\vec{r}(t) = 2 \cos t\vec{i} - 3 \sin t\vec{j}$

$\Rightarrow x = 2 \cos t, \ y = -3 \sin t$

$\Rightarrow \dfrac{x^2}{4} + \dfrac{y^2}{9} = \dfrac{4 \cos^2 t}{4} + \dfrac{9 \sin^2 t}{9} = \cos^2 t + \sin^2 t$

$\Rightarrow \dfrac{x^2}{4} + \dfrac{y^2}{9} = 1$

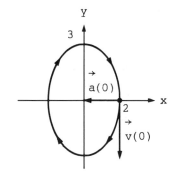

$\vec{v}(t) = \vec{r}'(t)$

$= -2 \sin t\vec{i} - 3 \cos t\vec{j}$

$\vec{a}(t) = \vec{r}''(t)$

$= -2 \cos t\vec{i} + 3 \sin t\vec{j}$

$\vec{v}(0) = -3\vec{j}$

$\vec{a}(0) = -2\vec{i}$

11. $\vec{r}(t) = (2 \cos t)\vec{i} + (3 \sin t)\vec{j}, \quad \vec{v}(t) = \vec{r}'(t)$

$= (-2 \sin t)\vec{i} + (3 \cos t)\vec{j}, \quad \vec{a}(t) = (-2 \cos t)\vec{i}$

$- (3 \sin t)\vec{j}, \quad \text{speed} = \|\vec{v}(t)\| = \sqrt{4 \sin^2 t + 9 \cos^2 t}$

15. $\vec{r}(t) = (3 \cos t)\vec{i} + (3 \sin t)\vec{j} + 5\vec{k}, \quad \vec{v}(t) = \vec{r}'(t)$

$= (-3 \sin t)\vec{i} + (3 \cos t)\vec{j}, \quad \vec{a}(t) = \vec{r}''(t)$

$= (-3 \cos t)\vec{i} - (3 \sin t)\vec{j}, \quad \text{speed} = \|\vec{v}(t)\|$

$= \sqrt{9 \sin^2 t + 9 \cos^2 t} = 3\sqrt{\sin^2 t + \cos^2 t} = 3$

19. $\vec{r}(t) = (\ln t)\vec{i} + \sqrt{t}\, \vec{j} + t^{3/2}\vec{k}, \quad t > 0,$

$\vec{v}(t) = \vec{r}'(t) = \frac{1}{t} \vec{i} + \frac{1}{2\sqrt{t}} \vec{j} + \frac{3}{2} \sqrt{t}\, \vec{k},$

$\vec{a}(t) = \vec{r}''(t) = -\frac{1}{t^2} \vec{i} - \frac{1}{4(\sqrt{t})^3} + \frac{3}{4\sqrt{t}} \vec{k},$

$\text{speed} = \|\vec{v}(t)\| = \sqrt{\frac{1}{t^2} + \frac{1}{4t} + \frac{9t}{4}} = \sqrt{\frac{4 + t + 9t^3}{4t^2}}$

$= \frac{\sqrt{9t^3 + t + 4}}{2t}$

23. See Example 4.

(a) $\|\vec{F}\| = m\|\vec{a}\| = \frac{mv_0^2}{R} \Longrightarrow$ triple speed, substitute

$3v_0$ for $v_0 \Longrightarrow$ new force magnitude $= \frac{m(3v_0)^2}{R}$

$= \frac{9mv_0^2}{R} = 9\|\vec{F}\|$. She must pull nine times as

hard on the rope.

(b) Double R but keep v_0 as at the start

$\Longrightarrow \frac{mv_0^2}{2R} = \frac{1}{2} \frac{mv_0^2}{R} = \frac{1}{2}\|\vec{F}\| \Longrightarrow$ she must pull less

than before (by $\frac{1}{2}$).

27. v_0 = distance/time = 1 circular orbit/1.5 hr

$= \dfrac{2 \pi R}{1.5 \text{ hr}} = \dfrac{4}{3} \pi R.$ From (15.8), $R = \dfrac{v_0^2}{g} = \dfrac{(4/3 \pi R)^2}{g}$

$\Rightarrow Rg = \dfrac{16}{9} \pi^2 R^2 \Rightarrow R = \dfrac{9g}{16 \pi^2} = \dfrac{9(79,036)}{16 \pi^2} \approx 4504.5$

miles (radius of earth $\approx$ 4000 miles) $\Rightarrow$ height of
orbit $\approx$ 504.5 miles.

31. See Example 4. v_0 = 200 km/hr, R = 75 m, mass = 1000 kg.

$\|\vec{F}\| = m(\dfrac{v_0^2}{g}) = 1000 \text{ kg}(\dfrac{200^2 \text{km}^2/\text{hr}^2}{75 \text{ m}})$

$= 1000(\dfrac{200^2}{75})\dfrac{1000^2}{3600^2}\dfrac{\text{kg m}}{\text{sec}^2} = 41,152 \text{ newtons}$

35. Instantaneous rate of change of angular momentum

$\vec{L}(t)$ with respect to time $= \dfrac{d[\vec{L}(t)]}{dt} = [\vec{r}(t) \times m\vec{v}(t)]'$

$= \vec{r}\,'(t) \times m\vec{v}(t) + \vec{r}(t) \times m\vec{v}\,'(t)$ (by (15.4d))

$= \vec{v}(t) \times m\vec{v}(t) + \vec{r}(t) \times m\vec{a}(t)$

$= m[\vec{v}(t) \times \vec{v}(t)] + \vec{r}(t) \times \vec{F}(t)$ (by (14.27b))

$= m(\vec{0}) + \vec{r}(t) \times \vec{F}(t)$ (by (14.27a))

$= \vec{r}(t) \times \vec{F}(t) = \vec{\tau}(t)$ = torque

Exercise 3, p. 840

3. $\vec{r}(t) = t\vec{i} + e^t\vec{j}$

$\Rightarrow x = t, \ y = e^t \Rightarrow y = e^x$

$\vec{v}(t) = \vec{r}\,'(t) = \vec{i} + e^t\vec{j}$

$v = \|\vec{v}(t)\| = \sqrt{1 + e^{2t}}$

$\vec{a}(t) = \vec{r}\,''(t) = e^t\vec{j}$

$\|\vec{a}(t)\| = \sqrt{0^2 + e^{2t}} = e^t$

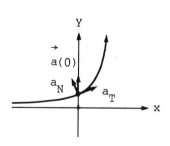

$$a_T = \frac{dv}{dt} = \frac{1}{2}(1+e^{2t})^{-\frac{1}{2}}(2e^{2t})$$

$$= \frac{e^{2t}}{\sqrt{1 + e^{2t}}}$$

$$a_N = \sqrt{\|\vec{a}(t)\|^2 - a_T^2}$$

$$= \sqrt{e^{2t} - \frac{e^{4t}}{1 + e^{2t}}} = \sqrt{\frac{e^{2t} + e^{4t} - e^{4t}}{1 + e^{2t}}}$$

$$= \frac{e^t}{\sqrt{1 + e^{2t}}}$$

$$\vec{a}(0) = \vec{j}$$

$$a_T(0) = \frac{e^0}{\sqrt{1 + e^0}} = 1/\sqrt{2}$$

$$a_N(0) = \frac{e^0}{\sqrt{1 + e^0}} = 1/\sqrt{2}$$

7. $\vec{r} = 2 \cos t\vec{i} - 3 \sin t\vec{j}$

=> $x = 2 \cos t$, $y = -3 \sin t$

=> $\frac{x^2}{4} + \frac{y^2}{9} = 1$

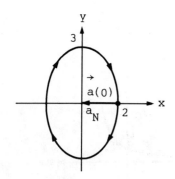

$$\vec{v}(t) = \vec{r}'(t)$$

$$= -2 \sin t\vec{i} - 3 \cos t\vec{j}$$

$$w = \|\vec{v}(t)\| = \sqrt{4 \sin^2 t + 9 \cos^2 t}$$

$$= \sqrt{4(\sin^2 t + \cos^2 t) + 5 \cos^2 t}$$

$$= \sqrt{4 + 5 \cos^2 t}$$

$$\vec{a}(t) = -2 \cos t\vec{i} + 3 \sin t\vec{j}$$

$$\|a(t)\| = \sqrt{4 \cos^2 t + 9 \sin^2 t}$$

$$= \sqrt{4(\cos^2 t + \sin^2 t) + 5 \sin^2 t}$$

$$= \sqrt{4 + 5 \sin^2 t}$$

$$a_T = \frac{dv}{dt} = \frac{1}{2}(4+5 \cos^2 t)^{-\frac{1}{2}}(-10 \cos t \sin t)$$

$$= -\frac{5 \cos t \sin t}{\sqrt{4 + 5 \cos^2 t}}$$

$$a_N = \sqrt{\|\vec{a}(t)\| - a_T{}^2}$$

$$= \sqrt{(4+5 \sin^2 t) - \frac{25 \cos^2 t \sin^2 t}{4 + 5 \cos^2 t}}$$

$$= \sqrt{\frac{16 + 20 \cos^2 t + 20 \sin^2 t}{4 + 5 \cos^2 t}}$$

$$= \sqrt{\frac{36}{4 + 5 \cos^2 t}} = \frac{6}{\sqrt{4 + 5 \cos^2 t}}$$

$$\vec{a}(0) = -2\vec{i}$$

$$a_T(0) = \frac{0}{\sqrt{9}} = 0$$

$$a_N(0) = \frac{6}{\sqrt{9}} = 2$$

11. $\vec{r}(t) = (2 \cos t)\vec{i} + (3 \sin t)\vec{j}$

$\vec{v}(t) = \vec{r}'(t) = (-2 \sin t)\vec{i} + (3 \cos t)\vec{j} \Rightarrow$

$v = \|\vec{v}(t)\| = \sqrt{4\sin^2 t + 9\cos^2 t}$

$\vec{a}(t) = \vec{r}''(t) = (-2 \cos t)\vec{i} - (3 \sin t)\vec{j}$

$\Rightarrow \|\vec{a}\| = \sqrt{4 \cos^2 t + 9 \sin^2 t}$

$$a_T = \frac{dv}{dt} = \frac{-5 \sin t \cos t}{\sqrt{4 \sin^2 t + 9 \cos^2 t}}$$

$$a_N = \sqrt{\|\vec{a}\|^2 - a_T{}^2}$$

$$= \sqrt{4 \cos^2 t + 9 \sin^2 t - \frac{25 \sin^2 t \cos^2 t}{4 \sin^2 t + 9 \cos^2 t}}$$

$$= \sqrt{\frac{36 \sin^4 t + 72 \sin^2 t \cos^2 t + 36 \cos^2 t}{4 \sin^2 t + 9 \cos^2 t}}$$

$$= \sqrt{\frac{36(\sin^2 t + \cos^2 t)^2}{4 \sin^2 t + 9 \cos^2 t}} = \frac{6}{\sqrt{4 \sin^2 t + 9 \cos^2 t}}$$

15. $\vec{r}(t) = (\cos 2t)\vec{i} + (\sin 2t)\vec{j} - 5\vec{k}$

$\vec{v}(t) = \vec{r}'(t) = (-2 \sin 2t)\vec{i} + (2 \cos 2t)\vec{j}$

$\Rightarrow v = \|\vec{v}(t)\| = \sqrt{4 \sin^2 2t + 4 \cos^2 2t}$

$\qquad = 2\sqrt{\sin^2 2t + \cos^2 2t} = 2$

$\vec{a}(t) = \vec{r}''(t) = (-4 \cos 2t)\vec{i} - (4 \sin 2t)\vec{j}$

$\Rightarrow \|\vec{a}\| = \sqrt{16 \cos^2 2t + 16 \sin^2 2t} \quad 4\sqrt{\cos^2 2t + \sin^2 2t} = 4$

$$a_T = \frac{dv}{dt} = 0, \quad a_N = \sqrt{\|\vec{a}\|^2 - a_T^{\,2}} = \sqrt{16 - 0} = 4$$

19. $\vec{r}(t) = t\vec{i} + t^2\vec{j} + t^3\vec{k}$

$\vec{v}(t) = \vec{r}'(t) = \vec{i} + 2t\vec{j} + 3t^2\vec{k}$

$\Rightarrow v = \|\vec{v}(t)\| = \sqrt{1 + 4t^2 + 9t^4}$

$\vec{a}(t) = \vec{r}''(t) = 2\vec{j} + 6t\vec{k} \Rightarrow \|\vec{a}\| = \sqrt{4 + 36t^2}$

$$a_T = \frac{dv}{dt} = \frac{4t + 18t^3}{\sqrt{1 + 4t^2 + 9t^4}}$$

$$a_N = \sqrt{\|\vec{a}\|^2 - a_T^{\,2}} = \sqrt{4 + 36t^2 - \frac{(4t + 18t^3)^2}{1 + 4t^2 + 9t^4}}$$

$$= \sqrt{\frac{4 + 36t^2 + 16t^2 + 144t^4 + 36t^4 + 324t^6 - 16t^2 - 144t^4 - 324t^6}{1 + 4t^2 + 9t^4}}$$

$$= \sqrt{\frac{4 + 36t^2 + 36t^4}{1 + 4t^2 + 9t^4}} = \frac{2\sqrt{1 + 9t^2 + 9t^4}}{\sqrt{1 + 4t^2 + 9t^4}}$$

Exercise 4, pp. 843-846

3. $\int [(\cos t)\vec{i} + (\sin t)\vec{j} - \vec{k}]dt = (\sin t)\vec{i} - (\cos t)\vec{j}$
$\quad - t\vec{k} + \vec{c}$

7. $\vec{v}(t) = \int \vec{a}(t)dt = \int[(\cos t)\vec{i} + (\sin t)\vec{j}]dt$

$= (\sin t)\vec{i} - (\cos t)\vec{j} + \vec{c}$

$\vec{v}(0) = \vec{i} \Rightarrow -\vec{j} + \vec{c} = \vec{i} \Rightarrow \vec{c} = \vec{i} + \vec{j} \Rightarrow$

$\vec{v}(t) = (\sin t + 1)\vec{i} + (-\cos t + 1)\vec{j} \Rightarrow$

speed $= \|\vec{v}(t)\| = \sqrt{(\sin t + 1)^2 + (-\cos t + 1)^2}$

$= \sqrt{\sin^2 t + \cos^2 t + 2 \sin t - 2 \cos t + 1 + 1}$

$= \sqrt{3 + 2 \sin t - 2 \cos t}$

$\vec{r}(t) = \int \vec{v}(t)dt = \int[(\sin t + 1)\vec{i} + (-\cos t + 1)\vec{j}]dt$

$= (-\cos t + t)\vec{i} + (-\sin t + t)\vec{j} + \vec{d}$

$\vec{r}(0) = j \Rightarrow -\vec{i} + \vec{d} = \vec{j} \Rightarrow \vec{d} = \vec{i} + \vec{j}$

$\Rightarrow \vec{r}(t) = (-\cos t + t + 1)\vec{i} + (-\sin t + t + 1)\vec{j}$

1. $v_0 = 520$ m/sec, $\theta = 30°$, $g = 9.8$ m/sec^2

From (15.21), range $= \dfrac{v_0^2 \sin 2\theta}{g} = \dfrac{(520)^2 \sin 60°}{9.8}$

$\approx 23,895$ m

From (15.22), time in flight $= \dfrac{2v_0 \sin \theta}{g} = \dfrac{2(520)\sin 30°}{9.8}$

≈ 53.1 sec

From (15.23), maximum height $= \dfrac{v_0^2 \sin^2\theta}{2g}$

$= \dfrac{(520)^2(\sin 30°)^2}{2(9.8)}$

≈ 3449 m

5. $x = \dfrac{v_0^2 \sin 2\theta}{g} \Rightarrow \dfrac{dx}{d\theta} = \dfrac{v_0^2}{g}(2 \cos 2\theta) = 0 \Rightarrow \cos 2\theta = 0 \Rightarrow \theta = \dfrac{\pi}{4};$

$\dfrac{dx}{d\theta} > 0$ for $0 < \theta < \dfrac{\pi}{4}$ and $\dfrac{dx}{d\theta} < 0$ for $\dfrac{\pi}{4} < \theta < \dfrac{\pi}{2} \Rightarrow$

x has a maximum at $\theta = \dfrac{\pi}{4} \Rightarrow$ the maximum value is

$\dfrac{v_0^2 \sin 2(\pi/4)}{g} = \dfrac{v_0^2}{g}$

19. $\vec{v}(0) = \vec{v}_0 = 3\vec{i} + 4\vec{j}$, $\vec{r}(0) = \vec{i} + 2\vec{j}$

$\vec{F} = m(-\vec{i} - \vec{j})/\sqrt{2} = m\vec{a}(t) \Rightarrow \vec{a}(t) = (1/\sqrt{2})(-\vec{i} - \vec{j})$

$\vec{v}(t) = \int \vec{a}(t)dt = -\dfrac{1}{\sqrt{2}}t\vec{i} - \dfrac{1}{\sqrt{2}}t\vec{j} + \vec{c}$, $\vec{v}(0) = \vec{c} = 3\vec{i} + 4\vec{j}$

$\Rightarrow \vec{v}(t) = (-\dfrac{1}{\sqrt{2}}t + 3)\vec{i} + (-\dfrac{1}{\sqrt{2}}t + 4)\vec{j}$

$\Rightarrow \vec{r}(t) = \int \vec{r}(t)dt = (-\dfrac{1}{2\sqrt{2}}t^2 + 3t)\vec{i} + (-\dfrac{1}{2\sqrt{2}}t^2 + 4t)\vec{j} + \vec{d}$

$\vec{r}(0) = \vec{d} = \vec{i} + 2\vec{j} \Rightarrow$

$\vec{r}(t) = (-\dfrac{1}{2\sqrt{2}}t^2 + 3t + 1)\vec{i} + (-\dfrac{1}{2\sqrt{2}}t^2 + 4t + 2)\vec{j}$

23. Set the origin at 6 ft.; then with $\theta = 45°$, v_0 = 100 ft./sec., $g = 32$ ft./sec^2, $y = -6$ ft. ("ground" level), and x = unknown, let's substitute into (15.19):

$x = v_0(\cos \theta)t = 100(\dfrac{1}{\sqrt{2}})t = \dfrac{100\,t}{\sqrt{2}} = 50\sqrt{2}\ t$

$y = -\dfrac{1}{2}gt^2 + v_0(\sin \theta)t$

$\Rightarrow -6 = -\dfrac{1}{2}(32)t^2 + 100(\dfrac{1}{\sqrt{2}})t$

$\Rightarrow 16t^2 - 50\sqrt{2}t - 6 = 0$

$\Rightarrow t = \dfrac{50\sqrt{2} \pm \sqrt{(50\sqrt{2})^2 - 4(16)(-6)}}{2(16)}$

$t = \dfrac{50\sqrt{2} \pm \sqrt{5384}}{32} = t \approx 4.50$ sec.

or $t \approx -.08$ sec.

Clearly, the only solution of interest is $t \approx 4.50$ sec. Substituting this into $x = 50\sqrt{2}t$, we find $x \approx 318.2$ ft.

The outfielder can be at most 318.2 ft. from home plate and the ball is in the air for 4.5 sec.

27. $\vec{r}'(t) = \vec{0} \Rightarrow \vec{r}(t) = \int \vec{r}'(t)dt = \vec{c}$, a constant, where the integration is done individually on each component.

Exercise 5, pp. 851-852

3. $\vec{r}(t) = (\sin 2t)\vec{i} + (\cos 2t)\vec{j} + t\vec{k}$

$\Rightarrow \vec{r}'(t) = (2\cos 2t)\vec{i} - (2\sin 2t)\vec{j} + \vec{k}$

$\Rightarrow \|\vec{r}'(t)\| = \sqrt{4\cos^2 2t + 4\sin^2 2t + 1}$

$= \sqrt{4(\cos^2 2t + \sin^2 2t) + 1} = \sqrt{5}$

$s = \int_0^\pi \|\vec{r}'(t)\|dt = \int_0^\pi \sqrt{5}\ dt = \sqrt{5}\ t\Big|_0^\pi = \pi\sqrt{5}$

7. $\vec{r}(t) = t\vec{i} + 2t\vec{j} + t\vec{k} \Rightarrow \vec{r}'(t) = \vec{i} + 2\vec{j} + \vec{k}$

$\Rightarrow \vec{r}''(t) = \vec{0}$

$\vec{r}'(t) \times \vec{r}''(t) = \vec{0} \Rightarrow \|\vec{r}'(t) \times \vec{r}''(t)\| = 0$

$\|\vec{r}'(t)\|^3 = (\sqrt{6})^3 = 6\sqrt{6}$

$\kappa = \dfrac{\|\vec{r}'(t) \times \vec{r}''(t)\|}{\|\vec{r}'(t)\|^3} = \dfrac{0}{6\sqrt{6}} = 0$

11. $\vec{r}(t) = e^t\vec{i} + e^{-t}\vec{j} + \sqrt{2}\ t\vec{k} \Rightarrow \vec{r}'(t) = e^t\vec{i} - e^{-t}\vec{j} + \sqrt{2}\ \vec{k}$

$\Rightarrow \vec{r}''(t) = e^t\vec{i} + e^{-t}\vec{j}$

$\vec{r}'(t) \times \vec{r}''(t) = \begin{vmatrix} \vec{i} & \vec{j} & \vec{k} \\ e^t & -e^{-t} & \sqrt{2} \\ e^t & e^{-t} & 0 \end{vmatrix}$

$= -\sqrt{2}\ e^{-t}\vec{i} + \sqrt{2}\ e^t\vec{j} + 2\vec{k}$

$\|\vec{r}'(t) \times \vec{r}''(t)\| = \sqrt{2e^{-2t} + 2e^{2t} + 4} = \sqrt{2(e^t + e^{-t})^2}$

$= \sqrt{2}(e^t + e^{-t})$

$\|\vec{r}'(t)\|^3 = \left(\sqrt{e^{2t} + e^{-2t} + 2}\right)^3 = \left(\sqrt{(e^t + e^{-t})^2}\right)^3$

$= (e^t + e^{-t})^3$

$$\kappa = \frac{\vec{r}'(t) \times \vec{r}''(t)}{\|\vec{r}'(t)\|^3} = \frac{\sqrt{2}(e^t + e^{-t})}{(e^t + e^{-t})^3} = \frac{\sqrt{2}}{(e^t + e^{-t})^2}$$

15. $\vec{r}(t) = (1-t^3)\vec{i} + t^2\vec{j} \Rightarrow \vec{r}'(t) = 3t^2\vec{i} + 2t\vec{j}$

$\Rightarrow \vec{r}''(t) = -6t\vec{i} + 2\vec{j}$

$$\vec{r}'(t) \times \vec{r}''(t) = \begin{vmatrix} \vec{i} & \vec{j} & \vec{k} \\ -3t^2 & 2t & 0 \\ -6t & 2 & 0 \end{vmatrix} = 6t\,\vec{k}$$

$\|\vec{r}'(t) \times \vec{r}''(t)\| = 6t^2$

$\|\vec{r}'(t)\|^3 = (\sqrt{9t^4+4t^2})^3 = (9t^4+4t^2)\sqrt{9t^4+4t^2}$

$$\kappa = \frac{\|\vec{r}'(t) \times \vec{r}''(t)\|}{\|\vec{r}'(t)\|^3} = \frac{6t^2}{(9t^4+4t^2)\sqrt{9t^4+4t^2}}$$

$$= \frac{6}{(9t^2+4)|t|\sqrt{9t^2+4}} = \frac{6}{|t|(9t^2+4)^{3/2}} \text{ or } \frac{6}{[t^2(9t^2+4)^3]^{1/2}}$$

The curvature is undefined at t=0.

From (13.13), $\dfrac{dy}{dx} = \dfrac{dy/dt}{dx/dt} = \dfrac{2t}{-3t^2} = \dfrac{-2}{3t}$, so the

tangent is undefined at t=0 and hence, by the development of curvature in Chapter 13, Section 8, curvature would be undefined.

19. $\vec{r}(t) = (\cos t)\vec{i} + (\sin t)\vec{j} = t\vec{k}$

$\vec{r}'(t) = (-\sin t)\vec{i} + (\cos t)\vec{j} + \vec{k}$

$\vec{r}''(t) = (-\cos t)\vec{i} - (\sin t)\vec{j}$

$$\vec{r}'(t) \times \vec{r}''(t) = \begin{vmatrix} \vec{i} & \vec{j} & \vec{k} \\ -\sin t & \cos t & 1 \\ -\cos t & -\sin t & 0 \end{vmatrix}$$

$$= (\sin t)\vec{i} - (\cos t)\vec{j} + (\sin^2 t + \cos^2 t)\vec{k}$$

$$= (\sin t)\vec{i} - (\cos t)\vec{j} + \vec{k}$$

$$\|\vec{r}'(t) \times \vec{r}''(t)\| = \sqrt{\sin^2 t + \cos^2 t + 1} = \sqrt{2}$$

$$v = \text{speed} = \|\vec{v}(t)\| = \|\vec{r}'(t)\| = \sqrt{\sin^2 t + \cos^2 t + 1} = \sqrt{2}$$

$$\|\vec{r}'(t)\|^3 = (\sqrt{2})^3 = 2\sqrt{2}$$

$$a_N = \kappa \vec{v}^2 = \frac{\|\vec{r}'(t) \times \vec{r}''(t)\|}{\|\vec{r}'(t)\|^3}(v^2) = \frac{\sqrt{2}}{2\sqrt{2}}(\sqrt{2})^2 = 1$$

23. $\dfrac{d\vec{T}}{ds} = \dfrac{d\vec{T}}{dt} \cdot \dfrac{dt}{ds}$ (chain rule)

From problem 22, $\vec{T} = \dfrac{1}{\sqrt{1 + (f')^2}}\vec{i} + \dfrac{f'}{\sqrt{1 + (f')^2}}\vec{j}$

Thus, $\dfrac{d\vec{T}}{dt} = -\dfrac{1}{2}(1+(f')^2)^{-3/2}(2f'f'')\vec{i}$

$$+ \frac{\sqrt{1 + (f')^2}\, f'' - f' \cdot \frac{1}{2}(1+(f')^2)^{-1/2} \cdot 2 \cdot f'f''}{(\sqrt{1+(f')^2})^2}\vec{j}$$

$$= \frac{-f'f''}{(\sqrt{1+(f')^2})^3}\vec{i} + \frac{(1+(f')^2)f'' - (f')^2 f''}{(\sqrt{1+(f')^2})^3}\vec{j}$$

$$= \frac{f''}{(\sqrt{1+(f')^2})^3}[-f'\vec{i} + \vec{j}]$$

From problem 21, $\dfrac{dt}{ds} = \dfrac{1}{\sqrt{1 + (f')^2}}$

Therefore,

$$\frac{d\vec{T}}{ds} = \frac{d\vec{T}}{dt} \cdot \frac{dt}{ds} = \frac{f''}{(1+(f')^2)^2}[-f'\vec{i} + \vec{j}].$$

Exercise 6, p. 856

3. For Pluto, $R = 39.5r$, $r =$ the earth's mean distance from the sun. Let $P =$ Pluto's period, $E =$ the earth's period $= 1$ year. Assuming the orbits to be circles and applying Kepler's Third Law yields:

$P^2 = cR^3$ and $E^2 = cr^3$ with $R = 39.5r$; then

$P^2 = cR^3 = c(39.5r)^3 = (39.5)^3 cr^3 = (39.5)^3 E^2$

$= (39.5)^3$ square earth years and $P \approx 248.25$ earth years.

3. $\vec{r} = (\sin^2 t)\vec{i} + (\tan t)\vec{j}, \quad -\pi/2 < t < \pi/2;$

   $x = \sin^2 t, \quad y = \tan t \implies 1 - x = 1 - \sin^2 t = \cos^2 t,$

   $y^2 = \dfrac{\sin^2 t}{\cos^2 t} \implies y^2 = \dfrac{x}{1-x}, \quad 0 \leq x < 1$

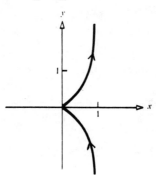

7. (a) $\vec{r}(t) = (4\cos t)\vec{i} - (2\cos 2t)\vec{j} \implies x = 4\cos t,$

    $y = -2\cos 2t \implies y = -2(2\cos^2 t - 1) = -2[2(\tfrac{x}{4})^2 - 1]$

    $= \dfrac{-x^2}{4} + 2 \implies x^2 = -4(y-2),$ parabola, vertex at

    $(0,2)$, opens down. $-4 \leq x \leq 4$ and $-2 \leq y \leq 2$.

    Typical oscillation:

t	cos t	x
$-\pi \to 0$	$-1 \to +1$	$-4 \to +4$
$0 \to \pi$	$+1 \to -1$	$+4 \to -4$

    (b)

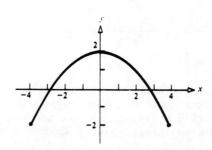

(c) $\vec{v}(t) = \vec{r}'(t) = (-4 \sin t)\vec{i} + (4 \sin 2t)\vec{j}$

$\vec{v}(t) = \vec{0} \Rightarrow -4 \sin t = 0$ and $4 \sin 2t = 0$

$\Rightarrow t = k\pi, \; k = $ integer

$\vec{a}(t) = \vec{r}''(t) = (-4 \cos t)\vec{i} + (8 \cos 2t)\vec{j}$

$\vec{a}(t) = -4\vec{i} + 8\vec{j}$ for $t = k\pi$ if k is even

$\vec{a}(t) = 4\vec{i} + 8\vec{j}$ for $t = k\pi$ if k is odd

11. $y = 3x^2 - x^3$ with $\vec{v}(t) = \frac{1}{3}\vec{i} + g(t)\vec{j}$

$\Rightarrow \vec{r}(t) = \int \vec{v}(t)dt = (\frac{1}{3}t + c_1)\vec{i} + [\int g(t)dt]\vec{j},$

c_1 a constant. Choose $x = \frac{1}{3}t$ (choose $c_1 = 0$),

then $y = 3(\frac{1}{3}t)^2 - (\frac{1}{3}t)^3 \Rightarrow y = \frac{1}{3}t^2 - \frac{1}{27}t^3$

$\Rightarrow \int g(t)dt = \frac{1}{3}t^2 - \frac{1}{27}t^3 \Rightarrow g(t) = \frac{2}{3}t - \frac{1}{9}t^2.$

$\vec{v}(t)$ horizontal $\Rightarrow g(t) = 0 \Rightarrow \frac{2}{3}t - \frac{1}{9}t^2$

$= \frac{1}{9}t(6-t) = 0 \Rightarrow t = 0$ or $t = 6$ (that is, $x = 0$

or $x = 2$). Since $\vec{v}(t) = \frac{1}{3}\vec{i} + (\frac{2}{3}t - \frac{1}{9}t^2)\vec{j},$

$\vec{a}(t) = (\frac{2}{3} - \frac{2}{9}t)\vec{j}.$ So at $x = 0$ $(t=0)$, $\vec{a} = \frac{2}{3}\vec{j}$,

at $x = 2$ $(t=6)$, $\vec{a} = \frac{2}{3}\vec{j}.$

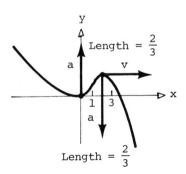

y

Length $= \frac{2}{3}$

a

v

x

1 3

a

Length $= \frac{2}{3}$

15. $\vec{r}(t) = t^2\vec{i} - 2\sqrt{2}t\vec{j} + (t^2-1)\vec{k}$

$\vec{r}'(t) = 2t\vec{i} - 2\sqrt{2}\vec{j} + 2t\vec{k}$

$\|\vec{r}'(t)\| = \sqrt{4t^2 + 8 + 4t^2} = 2\sqrt{2}\sqrt{t^2 + 1}$

Arc length $s = \int_0^1 \|\vec{r}'(t)\|dt = \int_0^1 2\sqrt{2}\sqrt{t^2+1}\,dt$

(use $t = \tan\theta$, $t^2 + 1 = \sec^2\theta$)

$= \int_0^{\pi/4} 2\sqrt{2}\sec\theta(\sec^2\theta\,d\theta)$

$= 2\sqrt{2}\int_0^{\pi/4}\sec^3\theta\,d\theta$ (use (9.6))

$= 2\sqrt{2}(\frac{1}{2}\sec\theta\tan\theta$

$+ \frac{1}{2}\ln|\sec\theta + \tan\theta|)\Big|_0^{\pi/4}$

$= \sqrt{2}(\sqrt{2})(1) + \sqrt{2}\ln|\sqrt{2} + 1|$

$= 2 + \sqrt{2}\ln(\sqrt{2} + 1)$

19. $\vec{r}(t) = 2t\vec{i} + (2t-1)\vec{j} + t\vec{k}$

$\vec{r}'(t) = 2\vec{i} + 2\vec{j} + \vec{k}$

$\|\vec{r}'(t)\| = \sqrt{4 + 4 + 1} = \sqrt{9} = 3$

Make a small dummy variable change within the arc length interval in (15.26) and integrate from 0 to t instead of from a to b.

$s = \int_0^t \|\vec{r}'(q)\|dq = \int_0^t 3dq = 3q\Big|_0^t = 3t$ or $t = \frac{s}{3}$,

where s = arc length; thus,

$\vec{r}(s) = \frac{2}{3}s\vec{i} + (\frac{2}{3}s - 1)\vec{j} + \frac{1}{3}s\vec{k}$

23. $r = 2 + \cos t$, $\theta = 2t$

$\Rightarrow r' = -\sin t$, $r'' = -\cos t$ and $\theta' = 2$, $\theta'' = 0$.

From Problem 22, part (c), $\vec{v}(t) = -\sin t\,\vec{u}_r$

$+ 2(2+\cos t)\vec{u}_\theta$. From Problem 22, part (d),

$$\vec{a}(t) = [-\cos t - (2 + \cos t)(4)]\vec{u}_r$$

$$+[(2 + \cos t)(0) + 2(-\sin t)(2)]\vec{u}_\theta$$

$$\vec{a}(t) = (-8 - 5\cos t)\vec{u}_r - 4\sin t \ \vec{u}_\theta.$$

27. $\vec{r}(t) = \frac{1}{3} t^3 \vec{i} + (t-1)\vec{j} + 2\vec{k}$

$\Rightarrow \vec{r}'(t) = t^2\vec{i} + \vec{j} \Rightarrow \|\vec{r}'(t)\| = \sqrt{t^4 + 1}$

Arc length $s = \int_0^{1/2} \sqrt{t^4 + 1} \ dt$

From Problem 1, Exercise 9, Chapter 11,

$$\sqrt{1 + x^2} = 1 + \frac{1}{2} x^2 - \frac{1}{2^2 2!} x^4 + \frac{1 \cdot 3}{2^3 \cdot 3!} x^6$$

$$- \frac{1 \cdot 3 \cdot 5}{2^4 4!} x^8 + \cdots$$

Substituting t^2 for x yields

$$\sqrt{t^4 + 1} = 1 + \frac{1}{2} t^4 - \frac{1}{2^2 \cdot 2!} t^8 + \frac{1 \cdot 3}{2^3 \cdot 3!} t^{12} - \cdots$$

Integrating both sides yields

$$\int \sqrt{t^4 + 1} \ dt = t + \frac{1}{5 \cdot 2} t^5 - \frac{1}{9 \cdot 2^2 2!} t^9$$

$$+ \frac{1 \cdot 3}{13 \cdot 2^3 \cdot 3!} t^{13} - \cdots$$

By (11.34), the error from using the first n terms is smaller than the (n+1)st term. Thus, for five-decimal-place accuracy, use the first 3 terms [since the 4th term = $(1/208)(0.5)^{13} \approx 0.0000006$]

$$\int_0^{1/2} \sqrt{t^4 + 1} \ dt \approx 0.5 + \frac{1}{10}(0.5)^5 - \frac{1}{72}(0.5)^9$$

$$\approx 0.5 + 0.003125 - 0.0000271$$

$$\approx 0.503098$$

Chapter Sixteen

Exercise 1, p. 863

3. $f(x,y) = \sqrt{xy} + x$

    (a) $f(0,0) = \sqrt{(0)(0)} + 0 = 0$

    (b) $f(0,1) = \sqrt{(0)(1)} + 0 = 0$

    (c) $f(a^2,t^2) = \sqrt{a^2 t^2} + a^2 = at + a^2$, $a > 0$, $t > 0$

    (d) $f(x + \Delta x, y) = \sqrt{(x + \Delta x)y} + x + \Delta x$

    (e) $f(x, y + \Delta y) = \sqrt{x(y + \Delta y)} + x$

7. $F(x,y) = e^{x^2+y^2}$, $g(x) = x^2$, $h(y) = 2y - 1$

$$F(g(x),h(y)) = F(x^2, 2y-1) = e^{(x^2)^2 + (2y-1)^2}$$
$$= e^{x^4 + (2y-1)^2}$$

11. $z = f(x,y) = \sqrt{xy}$

    Domain of $f = \{(x,y): xy \geq 0\}$

                $= \{(x,y): x \geq 0,\ y \geq 0\ \text{ or }\ x \leq 0,\ y \leq 0\}$

15. $z = f(x,y) = \dfrac{x}{\sqrt{x^2 + y^2 - 4}}$

    Domain $f = \{(x,y): x^2 + y^2 - 4 > 0\}$

               $= \{(x,y): x^2 + y^2 > 4\}$

This domain, as shown, is the set of all points exterior to a circle of radius 2 centered at the origin.

19. $w = f(x,y,z) = \dfrac{z \sin x}{\cos y}$. Since the domain of each

function in the numerator is all real numbers, we have

Domain $f = \{(x,y,z): \cos y \neq 0\}$

$$= \{(x,y,z): y \neq \frac{(2k + 1)\pi}{2} \text{ for } k \text{ any integer}\}$$

23. Suppose that the depth of the box is z centimeters, that the sides which cost \$3 per square centimeter are y centimeters in length, and that the less expensive sides are x centimeters in length. Then

    Cost = $C(x,y,z) = (4xy + 6yz + 4xz)$ dollars

Exercise 2, p. 870

3. $z = f(x,y) = \sqrt{1 - x^2 - y^2}$

   (Scale reduced on inner circles for clarity.)

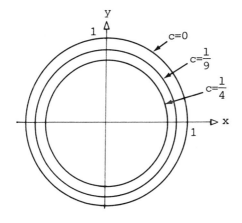

7. $z = f(x,y) = x + \sin y$

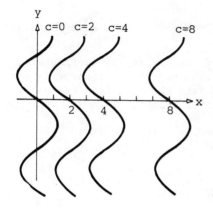

11. $f(x,y,z) = z - 2x - 2y$.

The level surfaces are parallel planes which have the normal vector $-2\vec{i} - 2\vec{j} + \vec{k}$.

15. $V(x,y) = \dfrac{9}{\sqrt{4 - (x^2 + y^2)}}$

The surface has the shape of a tube centered on the z-axis, infinitely long in the positive direction with radius approaching 2. The tube terminates with a rounded end (see diagram).

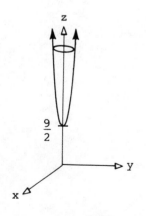

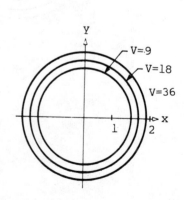

3. $f(x,y) = \dfrac{x^3}{y^3} = x^3 y^{-3}$ 7. $f(x,y) = e^{2x + 3y}$

   $f_x = 3x^2 y^{-3}$ $f_x = 2e^{2x + 3y}$

   $f_y = -3x^3 y^{-4}$ $f_y = 3e^{2x + 3y}$

11. $f(x,y) = \sin^2(2xy)$

   Using the chain rule twice, we have

   $f_x = 2\sin(2xy)\cos(2xy)(2y) = 4y\sin(2xy)\cos(2xy)$

   $ = 2y\sin(4xy)$

   Similarly,

   $f_y = 2\sin(2xy)\cos(2xy)(2x) = 4x\sin(2xy)\cos(2xy)$

   $ = 2x\sin(4xy)$

15. $f(x,y) = 6x^2 - 8xy + 9y^2$

   $f_x = 12x - 8y$

   $f_y = -8x + 18y$

   Hence, $f_{xx} = 12$

   $\ f_{yy} = 18$

   $\ f_{xy} = -8$

   $\ f_{yx} = -8$

19. $f(x,y) = e^{2x + 3y}$

   $f_x = 2e^{2x + 3y}$

   $f_y = 3e^{2x + 3y}$

   Hence, $f_{xx} = 4e^{2x + 3y}$

   $\ f_{yy} = 9e^{2x + 3y}$

   $\ f_{xy} = 6e^{2x + 3y}$

   $\ f_{yx} = 6e^{2x + 3y}$

23. $f(x,y,z) = xy + yz + xz$

$f_x = y + z$

$f_y = x + z$

$f_z = x + y$

27. $f(x,y,z) = z \tan^{-1}(\frac{y}{x})$

$f_x = (\frac{z}{1 + (y/x)^2})(-\frac{y}{x^2}) = \frac{-zy}{x^2 + y^2}$

$f_y = (\frac{z}{1 + (y/x)^2})(\frac{1}{x}) = \frac{xz}{x^2 + y^2}$

$f_z = \tan^{-1}(\frac{y}{x})$

31. $f(x,y,z) = x^{yz}$, $x > 0$

$f_x = yz(x^{yz-1})$

$f_y = z(\ell n \ x)x^{yz}$

$f_z = y(\ell n \ x)x^{yz}$

Note: Remember that each variable not directly related to a partial derivative is considered to be a constant.

35. $f(x,y) = \begin{cases} \dfrac{x^3 + y^3}{x^2 + y^2} & \text{if} \quad (x,y) \neq (0,0) \\ \\ 0 & \text{if} \quad (x,y) = (0,0) \end{cases}$

$f_x(0,0) = \lim_{\Delta x \to 0} [\frac{f(\Delta x, 0) - f(0,0)}{\Delta x}]$

$= \lim_{\Delta x \to 0} [\frac{(\Delta x)^3/(\Delta x)^2 - 0}{\Delta x}] = \lim_{\Delta x \to 0} (\frac{\Delta x}{\Delta x}) = 1$

$f_y(0,0) = \lim_{\Delta y \to 0} [\frac{f(0, \Delta y) - f(0,0)}{\Delta y}]$

$= \lim_{\Delta y \to 0} [\frac{(\Delta y)^3/(\Delta y)^2 - 0}{\Delta y}] = \lim_{\Delta y \to 0} (\frac{\Delta y}{\Delta y}) = 1$

39. On the curve of intersection of the surface

$z = \sqrt{1 - x^2 - y^2}$ with $x = 0$, the slope at any point (except the endpoints) is

$f_y(x,y) = \dfrac{-y}{\sqrt{1 - x^2 - y^2}}$. At the point $(0, \frac{1}{2}, \frac{\sqrt{3}}{2})$,

the slope is $-\dfrac{1}{2}\sqrt{\dfrac{4}{3}} = -\dfrac{\sqrt{3}}{3}$. Hence, the tangent line

sought may be specified by $(z - \frac{\sqrt{3}}{2}) = -\frac{\sqrt{3}}{3}(y - \frac{1}{2})$,

$x = 0$. (See Example 3 for a similar problem.)

43. $z = \ell n\sqrt{x^2 + y^2} = \dfrac{1}{2}\,\ell n(x^2 + y^2)$

(a) $f_x(x,y) = \dfrac{x}{x^2 + y^2}$

Thus, at $(3,4,\ell n\,5)$ the rate of change sought

is $\dfrac{3}{9 + 16} = \dfrac{3}{25}$.

(b) $f_y(x,y) = \dfrac{y}{x^2 + y^2}$

Thus, at $(3,4,\ell n5)$ the rate of change sought

is $\dfrac{4}{9 + 16} = \dfrac{4}{25}$.

47. $x = r\cos\theta$, $y = r\sin\theta$

$\dfrac{\partial x}{\partial r} = \cos\theta \qquad \dfrac{\partial x}{\partial \theta} = -r\sin\theta$

$\dfrac{\partial y}{\partial r} = \sin\theta \qquad \dfrac{\partial y}{\partial \theta} = r\cos\theta$

51. $u = x^2 + 4y^2$

$\dfrac{\partial u}{\partial x} = 2x; \quad \dfrac{\partial u}{\partial y} = 8y$

$x(\dfrac{\partial u}{\partial x}) + y(\dfrac{\partial u}{\partial y}) = 2x^2 + 8y^2 = 2u$

55. $z = \cos(x+y) + \cos(x-y)$

$\dfrac{\partial z}{\partial x} = -\sin(x+y) - \sin(x-y)$

$\dfrac{\partial z}{\partial y} = -\sin(x+y) + \sin(x-y)$

$\dfrac{\partial^2 z}{\partial x^2} - \dfrac{\partial^2 z}{\partial y^2} = [-\cos(x+y) - \cos(x-y)]$

$\qquad\qquad\qquad - [-\cos(x+y) - \cos(x-y)] = 0$

59. $z = e^{x^2+y^2}/(x^2 + y^2)$

$\dfrac{\partial z}{\partial x} = \dfrac{2x(x^2+y^2)e^{x^2+y^2} - 2xe^{x^2+y^2}}{(x^2+y^2)^2} = \dfrac{2xe^{x^2+y^2}(x^2+y^2-1)}{(x^2+y^2)^2}$

By symmetry with respect to x and y,

$\dfrac{\partial z}{\partial y} = \dfrac{2ye^{x^2+y^2}(x^2+y^2-1)}{(x^2+y^2)^2}$

$y\,\dfrac{\partial z}{\partial x} = \dfrac{2xy\,e^{x^2+y^2}(x^2+y^2-1)}{(x^2+y^2)^2} = x\,\dfrac{\partial z}{\partial y}$

63. $v = k\sqrt{\dfrac{p}{d}}$, $k = $ constant

$\dfrac{\partial v}{\partial p} = k\cdot\dfrac{1}{2}(\dfrac{p}{d})^{-1/2}(\dfrac{1}{d}) = \dfrac{k}{2}\sqrt{\dfrac{1}{pd}} = \dfrac{k}{2\sqrt{pd}}$

$\dfrac{\partial v}{\partial d} = k\cdot\dfrac{1}{2}(\dfrac{p}{d})^{-1/2}(\dfrac{-p}{d^2}) = \dfrac{-k}{2}\sqrt{\dfrac{p}{d^3}}$

Exercise 4, pp. 887-889

3. $\lim\limits_{(x,y)\to(0,0)} \dfrac{x^2 - y^2}{x - y} = \lim\limits_{(x,y)\to(0,0)} \dfrac{(x-y)(x+y)}{(x-y)}$

$\qquad\qquad = \lim\limits_{(x,y)\to(0,0)} (x+y) = 0 + 0 = 0$

7. $\lim\limits_{(x,y,z)\to(0,0,1)} (\dfrac{x^2z - y^2z}{x - y}) = \lim\limits_{(x,y,z)\to(0,0,1)} (\dfrac{z(x-y)(x+y)}{x - y})$

$$= \lim_{(x,y,z)\to(0,0,1)} z(x+y) = 1(0+0) = 0$$

11. $\displaystyle\lim_{(x,y)\to(0,0)} \cos\left[\frac{x^2 + y^2}{x + y + 1}\right] = \cos[\frac{0}{1}] = \cos[0] = 1$

15. Along the x-axis the limit is

$$\lim_{(x,0)\to(0,0)} [\frac{2x^2 + 0^2}{x^2 + 0^2}] = \lim_{x\to 0} (\frac{2x^2}{x^2}) = 2$$

Along the y-axis, though, it is

$$\lim_{(0,y)\to(0,0)} [\frac{(2)0^2 + y^2}{0^2 + y^2}] = \lim_{y\to 0} (\frac{y^2}{y^2}) = 1$$

These are different, so the overall limit does not exist.

19. $f(x,y) = \dfrac{x^2 y}{x^2 - y^2}$. f is discontinuous at all points of the set

$\{(x,y): x^2 = y^2\}$ or $\{(x,y): x = \pm y\}$

23. $f(x,y,z) = (\dfrac{xyz}{1 + x^2 + y^2 + z^2})$. Since f is a rational function whose denominator can never be 0, f is continuous at all points (x,y,z) in three-space.

27. $f(x,y) = e^{x\ln y}$

$\quad f_x = (\ln y)e^{x\ln y}$

$\quad f_{xy} = \dfrac{1}{y}e^{x\ln y} + (\ln y)(x\cdot\dfrac{1}{y})e^{x\ln y}$

$\qquad = \dfrac{1}{y}e^{x\ln y}(1 + x\ln y)$

$\quad f_y = (x\cdot\dfrac{1}{y})e^{x\ln y} = \dfrac{x}{y}e^{x\ln y}$

$\quad f_{yx} = \dfrac{1}{y}e^{x\ln y} + \dfrac{x}{y}(\ln y)e^{x\ln y}$

Thus, $f_{xy} = f_{yx}$.

3. $z = f(x,y) = x \sin y + y \sin x$

   $dz = f_x \, dx + f_y \, dy$

   $\quad = (\sin y + y \cos x)dx + (x \cos y + \sin x)dy$

7. $z = f(x,y) = \ell n(x^2 + y^2)$

   $dz = f_x \, dx + f_y \, dy = \dfrac{2x \, dx + 2y \, dy}{x^2 + y^2}$

11. $w = f(x,y,z) = xe^{yz} + ye^{xz} + ze^{xy}$

   $dw = f_x \, dx + f_y \, dy + f_z dz = (e^{yz} + yze^{xz} + yze^{xy})dx$

   $\quad\quad + (xze^{yz} + e^{xz} + xze^{xy})dy + (xye^{yz} + xye^{xz} + e^{xy})dz$

15. $\Delta z = f(x+\Delta x, y+\Delta y) - f(x,y)$

   $\quad = (x+\Delta x)(y+\Delta y)^2 - 2(x+\Delta x)(y+\Delta y) - xy^2 + 2xy$

   $\quad = (x+\Delta x)(y^2 + 2y\Delta y + (\Delta y)^2) - 2(xy + x\Delta y + y\Delta x + \Delta x\Delta y)$

   $\quad\quad -xy^2 + 2xy$

   $\quad = (y^2 - 2y)\Delta x + (2xy - 2x)\Delta y + 2y\Delta x\Delta y + \Delta x(\Delta y)^2$

   $\quad\quad + x(\Delta y)^2 - 2\Delta x\Delta y$

   $\quad = f_x \, dx + f_y \, dy + (2y\Delta y + (\Delta y)^2 - 2\Delta y)\Delta x + (x\Delta y)\Delta y$

   This has the form: $dz + \eta_1 \Delta x + \eta_2 \Delta y$, with $\eta_1 \to 0$
   and $\eta_2 \to 0$ as $(\Delta x, \Delta y) \to (0,0)$.

19. $z = f(x,y) = x^2 + y^2$

   $dz = f_x \, dx + f_y \, dy = 2x\Delta x + 2y\Delta y$

   $\quad = 2(1)(0.1) + 2(3)(0.2) = 0.2 + 1.2 = 1.4$

23. Set $z = f(x,y) = \sqrt[4]{x} \ \sqrt[5]{y}$.
   We know $f(16,32) = \sqrt[4]{16} \ \sqrt[5]{32} = (2)(2) = 4$.
   Now $f(16.01, \ 32.1) \approx f(16,32) + dz$
   where $dz = f_x \, dx + f_y \, dy$

$$= \frac{1}{4} x^{-3/4} y^{\frac{1}{5}} \Delta x + \frac{1}{5} x^{\frac{1}{4}} y^{-4/5} \Delta y$$

$$= \frac{1}{4}(16)^{-3/4}(32)^{\frac{1}{5}}(0.01) + \frac{1}{5}(16)^{1/4}(32)^{-4/5}(0.1)$$

$$= \frac{2}{32}(0.01) + \frac{2}{80}(0.1) = 0.003125$$

Hence, $(\sqrt[4]{16.01})(\sqrt[5]{32.1}) \approx 4.003125$.

27. Area $A(b,a) = \frac{1}{2}ba$

$$dA = A_b\,db + A_a\,da = \frac{1}{2}(a\Delta b + b\Delta a)$$
$$= \frac{1}{2}[5(0.05) + 2(0.1)] = 0.225 \text{ cm}^2$$

31. $R = f(R_1,R_2) = \dfrac{1}{(1/R_1 + 1/R_2)} = \dfrac{R_1 R_2}{R_1 + R_2}$

We convert the percentage errors to

$\Delta R_1 = \pm 0.6$ ohm, $\quad \Delta R_2 = \pm 0.75$ ohm.

Now $dR = f_{R_1}\,dR_1 + f_{R_2}\,dR_2 = (\dfrac{1}{R_1 + R_2})^2 [R_2^2 \Delta R_1 + R_1^2 \Delta R_2]$,

which for the maximum equals

$$\pm\ (\frac{1}{125})^2 [(75)^2(0.6) + (50)^2(0.75)] = \pm\ \frac{8.4}{25} = \pm 0.336 \text{ ohm.}$$

Since $R = \dfrac{R_1 R_2}{R_1 + R_2} = \dfrac{(50)(75)}{125} = 30$ ohms,

this corresponds to a percentage error of about 1.1%.

35. Area $A(b,c,\alpha) = \frac{1}{2} bc \sin\alpha$

$$dA = A_b\,db + A_c\,dc + A_\alpha\,d\alpha = (\frac{1}{2} c \sin\alpha)db$$
$$+ (\frac{1}{2} b \sin\alpha)dc + (\frac{1}{2} bc \cos\alpha)d\alpha$$

(a) $\dfrac{dA}{A} = \dfrac{db}{b} + \dfrac{dc}{c} + \cot\alpha\,d\alpha$

(b)   Use the formula in (a) with $\dfrac{db}{b} = \dfrac{dc}{c} = 0.02$,

$\dfrac{d\alpha}{\alpha} = 0.03$, and $\alpha = \dfrac{\pi}{4}$. $\dfrac{dA}{A} \approx 0.02 + 0.02$

$+ (1)(\dfrac{\pi}{4})(0.03) \approx 0.06356$. Hence the maximum percentage error in the computation of A is 6.356%.

39.

$$f(x, y) = \begin{cases} \dfrac{x^2y^2}{x^4+y^4} & \text{if}(x, y) \neq (0, 0) \\[2ex] 0 & \text{if } (x, y) = (0, 0) \end{cases}$$

Using (16.2),

$f_x(0, 0) = \lim_{\Delta x \to 0} \dfrac{f(\Delta x, 0)-f(0, 0)}{\Delta x} = \lim_{\Delta x \to 0} \dfrac{0-0}{\Delta x} = 0$

$f_y(0, 0) = \lim_{\Delta y \to 0} \dfrac{f(0, \Delta y)-f(0, 0)}{\Delta y} = \lim_{\Delta y \to 0} \dfrac{0-0}{\Delta y} = y$

However, f is not even continuous at (0, 0), because if $(x,y) \to (0, 0)$ along the line y=x, f(x, y) approaches 1/2 (in fact, is identically 1/2). Yet, f(0, 0) = 0, so f is not continuous at (0, 0). By Theorem (16.21), f is not differentiable at (0, 0).

Exercise 6, pp. 907-908

3. $z = e^u \sin v$, $u = x^2y$, $v = \ell n(xy)$

$\dfrac{\partial z}{\partial x} = \dfrac{\partial z}{\partial u}\dfrac{\partial u}{\partial x} + \dfrac{\partial z}{\partial v}\dfrac{\partial v}{\partial x} = e^u \sin v(2xy) + e^u \cos v(\dfrac{1}{x})$

$= e^{x^2y}[2xy \sin(\ell n(xy)) + \dfrac{1}{x} \cos(\ell n(xy))]$

$\dfrac{\partial z}{\partial y} = \dfrac{\partial z}{\partial u}\dfrac{\partial u}{\partial y} + \dfrac{\partial z}{\partial v}\dfrac{\partial v}{\partial y} = e^u \sin v(x^2) + e^u \cos v(\dfrac{1}{y})$

$= e^{x^2y}[x^2\sin(\ell n(xy)] + \dfrac{1}{y} \cos[\ell n(xy)]]$

7. $z = uv^2w^3$, $u = 2x + y$, $v = 5x - 3y$, $w = 2x + 3y$

$\dfrac{\partial z}{\partial x} = \dfrac{\partial z}{\partial u}\dfrac{\partial u}{\partial x} + \dfrac{\partial z}{\partial v}\dfrac{\partial v}{\partial x} + \dfrac{\partial z}{\partial w}\dfrac{\partial w}{\partial x} = 2v^2w^3 + 10uvw^3 + 6uv^2w^2$

$$= 2(5x-3y)^2(2x+3y)^3 + 10(2x+y)(5x-3y)(2x+3y)^3$$

$$+ 6(2x+y)(5x-3y)^2(2x+3y)^2$$

$$\frac{\partial z}{\partial y} = \frac{\partial z}{\partial u}\frac{\partial u}{\partial y} + \frac{\partial z}{\partial v}\frac{\partial v}{\partial y} + \frac{\partial z}{\partial w}\frac{\partial w}{\partial y} = v^2w^3 - 6uvw^3 + 9uv^2w^2$$

$$= (5x-3y)^2(2x+3y)^3 - 6(2x+y)(5x-3y)(2x+3y)^3$$

$$+ 9(2x+y)(5x-3y)^2(2x+3y)^2$$

11. $z = u^2 + v^2$, $u = \sin(x-y)$, $v = \cos(x+y)$

$$\frac{\partial z}{\partial x} = \frac{\partial z}{\partial u}\frac{\partial u}{\partial x} + \frac{\partial z}{\partial v}\frac{\partial v}{\partial x}$$

$$= 2u \cdot \cos(x-y) + 2v \cdot (-\sin(x+y))$$

$$= 2\sin(x-y)\cos(x-y) - 2\cos(x+y)\sin(x+y)$$

$$\frac{\partial z}{\partial y} = \frac{\partial z}{\partial u}\frac{\partial u}{\partial y} + \frac{\partial z}{\partial v}\frac{\partial v}{\partial y}$$

$$= 2u \cdot (-\cos(x-y)) + 2v(-\sin(x+y))$$

$$= -2\sin(x-y)\cos(x-y) - 2\cos(x+y)\sin(x+y)$$

15. $z = e^u \sin v$, $y = \sqrt{t}$, $v = \pi t$

$$\frac{dz}{dt} = \frac{\partial z}{\partial u}\frac{du}{dt} + \frac{\partial z}{\partial v}\frac{dv}{dt} = (e^u \sin v)(1/2\sqrt{t}) + (e^u \cos v)(\pi)$$

$$= \frac{e^{\sqrt{t}}}{2\sqrt{t}}(\sin \pi t + 2\pi\sqrt{t} \cos \pi t)$$

19. $z = u^2vw^3$, $u = \sin t$, $v = \cos t$, $w = e^t$

$$\frac{dz}{dt} = \frac{\partial z}{\partial u}\frac{du}{dt} + \frac{\partial z}{\partial v}\frac{dv}{dt} + \frac{\partial z}{\partial w}\frac{dw}{dt}$$

$$= 2uvw^3\cos t + u^2w^3(-\sin t) + 3u^2vw^2e^t$$

$$= \sin t\, e^{3t}(2\cos^2 t - \sin^2 t + 3\sin t \cos t)$$

23. $F(x,y) = x^2y - y^2x + xy - 5 = 0$

$F_x = 2xy - y^2 + y$; $F_y = x^2 - 2xy + x$

$$\frac{dy}{dx} = -\frac{F_x}{F_y} = \frac{y(y-1-2x)}{x(x+1-2y)}$$

27. $F(x,y) = x^{1/3} + y^{1/3} - 1 = 0$

$$F_x = \frac{1}{3}x^{-2/3}; \quad F_y = \frac{1}{3}y^{-2/3}$$

$$\frac{dy}{dx} = -\frac{F_x}{F_y} = \frac{-x^{-2/3}}{y^{-2/3}} = -y^{2/3}/x^{2/3}$$

31. $F(x,y,z) = \sin z + y \cos z + xyz - 10 = 0$

$$F_x = yz; \quad F_y = \cos z + xz; \quad F_z = \cos z - y \sin z + xy$$

$$\frac{\partial z}{\partial x} = -\frac{F_x}{F_z} = \frac{yz}{y \sin z - xy - \cos z};$$

$$\frac{\partial z}{\partial y} = -\frac{F_y}{F_z} = \frac{\cos z + xz}{y \sin z - xy - \cos z}$$

35. $z = f(u,v)$ with $u = x - y$, $v = y - x$

$$\frac{\partial z}{\partial x} = \frac{\partial z}{\partial u}\frac{\partial u}{\partial x} + \frac{\partial z}{\partial v}\frac{\partial v}{\partial x} = \frac{\partial z}{\partial u} - \frac{\partial z}{\partial v}$$

$$\frac{\partial z}{\partial y} = \frac{\partial z}{\partial u}\frac{\partial u}{\partial y} + \frac{\partial z}{\partial v}\frac{\partial v}{\partial y} = -\frac{\partial z}{\partial u} + \frac{\partial z}{\partial v}$$

Hence, $\left(\frac{\partial z}{\partial x}\right) + \left(\frac{\partial z}{\partial y}\right) = 0$

39. $z = f(x,y)$, $x = u/v$, $y = v/w$

$$\frac{\partial z}{\partial u} = \frac{\partial f}{\partial x}\frac{\partial x}{\partial u} + \frac{\partial f}{\partial y}\frac{\partial y}{\partial u} = \frac{\partial f}{\partial x}\left(\frac{1}{v}\right) + \frac{\partial f}{\partial y}(0) = \frac{1}{v}\frac{\partial f}{\partial x}$$

$$\frac{\partial z}{\partial v} = \frac{\partial f}{\partial x}\frac{\partial x}{\partial v} + \frac{\partial f}{\partial y}\frac{\partial y}{\partial v} = \frac{\partial f}{\partial x}\left(\frac{-u}{v^2}\right) + \frac{\partial f}{\partial y}\left(\frac{1}{w}\right)$$

$$= \frac{-u}{v^2}\frac{\partial f}{\partial x} + \frac{1}{w}\frac{\partial f}{\partial y}$$

$$\frac{\partial z}{\partial w} = \frac{\partial f}{\partial x}\frac{\partial x}{\partial w} + \frac{\partial f}{\partial y}\frac{\partial y}{\partial w} = \frac{\partial f}{\partial x}(0) + \frac{\partial f}{\partial y}(\frac{-v}{w^2}) = \frac{-v}{w^2}\frac{\partial f}{\partial y}$$

Thus,

$$u\frac{\partial z}{\partial u} + v\frac{\partial z}{\partial v} + w\frac{\partial z}{\partial w} = \frac{u}{v}\frac{\partial f}{\partial x} + \frac{-u}{v}\frac{\partial f}{\partial x} + \frac{v}{w}\frac{\partial f}{\partial y} + \frac{-v}{w}\frac{\partial f}{\partial y} = 0$$

43. Let $z = f(x, y)$, a differentiable function, be
    defined implicitly by the equation $f(x, y, z) = 0$.
    Set $w = F(u, v, z)$, $u=x$, and $v=y$. Since
    $w = F(x, y, f(x, y)) = 0$, it follows that $\frac{\partial w}{\partial y} = 0$

Hence, $\frac{\partial w}{\partial y} = \frac{\partial F}{\partial u}\frac{\partial u}{\partial y} + \frac{\partial F}{\partial v}\frac{\partial v}{\partial y} + \frac{\partial F}{\partial z}\frac{\partial z}{\partial y} = 0$. Since $u=x$ and

$v=y$, we have

$$(\frac{\partial F}{\partial x})(0) + (\frac{\partial F}{\partial y})(1) + (\frac{\partial F}{\partial z}\frac{\partial z}{\partial y}) = 0.$$

If $\frac{\partial F}{\partial z} \neq 0$, this gives $\frac{\partial z}{\partial y} = -(\frac{\partial F}{\partial y})/(\frac{\partial F}{\partial z}) = -\frac{F_y(x, y, z)}{F_z(x, y, z)}$

47. $w = (2x)^{3y+4z}$

$\frac{\partial w}{\partial x} = 2(3y+4z)(2x)^{3y+4z-1}$, $\frac{\partial w}{\partial y} = 3[\ln(2x)](2x)^{3y+4z}$

$\frac{\partial w}{\partial z} = 4[\ln(2x)](2x)^{3y+4z}$

Miscellaneous Exercises, pp. 908-911

3. $F(x,y,z) = e^x \sin y + e^y \sin z$. First note:
   $F_x = e^x \sin y$, $F_y = e^x \cos y + e^y \sin z$, and
   $F_z = e^y \cos z$. Differentiating these again, we have:
   $F_{xx} = e^x \sin y$ $\qquad\qquad$ $F_{xy} = F_{yx} = e^x \cos y$

$$F_{yy} = -e^x \sin y + e^y \sin z \qquad F_{xz} = F_{zx} = 0$$

$$F_{zz} = -e^y \sin z \qquad\qquad F_{yz} = F_{zy} = e^y \cos z$$

7. (a) On the curve of intersection of the given surface with the plane $x = 1$, the slope at any point is $f_y(x,y) = -2y$. At the point $(1,-2,1)$, the slope is 4, so the tangent line is given by $(z-1) = 4(y+2)$, $x = 1$.

   (b) On the curve of intersection of the given surface with the plane $y = -2$, the slope at any point is $f_x(x,y) = 8x$. At the point $(1,-2,1)$, the slope is 8, so the tangent line is given by $(z-1) = 8(x-1)$, $y = -2$.

11. This set consists of all points in the upper half of the solid unit sphere, centered at the origin, which are interior to the circular cone $x^2 + y^2 = z^2$.

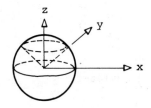

15. $x = r \cos \theta$, $y = r \sin \theta$

   $\dfrac{\partial x}{\partial r} = \cos \theta$, $\dfrac{\partial y}{\partial r} = \sin \theta$, $\dfrac{\partial x}{\partial \theta} = -r \sin \theta$, and

   $\dfrac{\partial y}{\partial \theta} = r \cos \theta$. Hence, the first determinant equals

   $(\dfrac{\partial x}{\partial r})(\dfrac{\partial y}{\partial \theta}) - (\dfrac{\partial x}{\partial \theta})(\dfrac{\partial y}{\partial r}) = r \cos^2\theta + r \sin^2\theta = r.$

   Next, since $r = \sqrt{x^2 + y^2}$ and $\theta = \tan^{-1} (\dfrac{y}{x})$,

   $\dfrac{\partial r}{\partial x} = \dfrac{x}{\sqrt{x^2 + y^2}} = \dfrac{x}{r}$, $\dfrac{\partial r}{\partial y} = \dfrac{y}{\sqrt{x^2 + y^2}} = \dfrac{y}{r}$,

$$\frac{\partial \theta}{\partial x} = \left(\frac{1}{1 + (\frac{y}{x})^2}\right)(-\frac{y}{x^2}) = \frac{-y}{x^2 + y^2} = -\frac{y}{r^2}, \quad \text{and}$$

$$\frac{\partial \theta}{\partial y} = \left(\frac{1}{1 + (\frac{y}{x})^2}\right)(\frac{1}{x}) = \frac{x}{x^2 + y^2} = \frac{x}{r^2}.$$

Hence, the second determinant equals

$$(\frac{\partial r}{\partial x})(\frac{\partial \theta}{\partial y}) - (\frac{\partial r}{\partial y})(\frac{\partial \theta}{\partial x}) = \frac{x^2}{r^3} + \frac{y^2}{r^3} = \frac{r^2}{r^3} = \frac{1}{r}.$$

19. No, these conditions are impossible, by Theorem (16.5)

If $f_x(x,y) = 2x - y$ and $f_y(x,y) = x - 2y$ for all

x and y, then $f_{xy}(x,y) = -1$, but $f_{yx}(x,y) = 1$.

The hypotheses of Theorem (16.5) would then be satisfied, so the mixed partials could not be different.

23. $y = \ln z$ or $z = e^y$

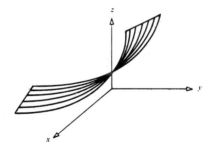

27.
$$f(x, y) = \begin{cases} e^{-1/(x^2+y^2)} & \text{if } (x, y) \neq (0, 0) \\ 0 & \text{if } (x, y) = (0, 0) \end{cases}$$

Using (16.2), $f_x(0, 0) = \lim_{\Delta x \to 0} \dfrac{f(\Delta x, 0) - f(0, 0)}{\Delta x}$

$$= \lim_{\Delta x \to 0} (\tfrac{1}{\Delta x})[e^{-1/(\Delta x)^2}]$$

$= \lim_{t \to +\infty} (te^{-t^2}) = 0$, by L'Hospital's rule. By symmetry

of f with respect to x and y, $f_y(0, 0) = 0$ also.

31. $f(x, y) = \dfrac{xy}{x+y}$. First note: $f_x = \dfrac{y(x+y)-xy}{(x+y)^2} = (\dfrac{y}{x+y})^2$

and by symmetry $f_y = (\dfrac{x}{x+y})^2$. Hence, $f_{xx} = \dfrac{-2y^2}{(x+y)^3}$,

$f_{yy} = \dfrac{-2x^2}{(x+y)^3}$, and $f_{xy} = \dfrac{2y}{(x+y)^2} - \dfrac{2y^2}{(x+y)^3} = \dfrac{2xy}{(x+y)^3}$.

Hence, $x^2 f_{xx} + 2xy f_{xy} + y^2 f_{yy}$

$= (x+y)^{-3}[-2x^2y^2 + 4x^2y^2 - 2x^2y^2)] = 0$.

35. Along the line $y = mx$, $f(x, y) = \dfrac{3x(mx)^2}{x^2+(mx)^4} = \dfrac{3m^2x^3}{x^2+m^4x^4}$

$= \dfrac{3m^2x}{1+m^4x^2}$. As $x \to 0$, this expression has limit 0,

regardless of m. Along the parabola $x = y^2$,

$f(x, y) = \dfrac{3y^4}{y^4+y^4} = \dfrac{3}{2}$. Thus, as $(x, y) \to (0, 0)$ along

this parabola, $f(x, y)$ approaches $3/2$ as a limit. Since

these two values are different, $\lim_{(x, y) \to (0, 0)} f(x, y)$

does not exist.

39. $f(x, y) = \sqrt{(x+2y)/(3x-y)}$. Taking logs, we have

$\ln(f) = \frac{1}{2}[\ln(x+2y) - \ln(3x-y)]$. Hence,

$\dfrac{f_x}{f} = \dfrac{1}{2}(\dfrac{1}{x+2y} - \dfrac{3}{3x-y})$, or $f_x = \dfrac{1}{2}f(\dfrac{1}{x+2y} - \dfrac{3}{3x-y})$. Also,

$\dfrac{f_y}{f} = \dfrac{1}{2}(\dfrac{2}{x+2y} - \dfrac{1}{3x-y})$, or $f_y = \dfrac{1}{2}f[\dfrac{2}{x+2y} + \dfrac{1}{3x-y}]$.

43. $f(x, y) = \int_x^y \ln(\cos\sqrt{t})dt = -\int_y^x \ln(\cos\sqrt{t})dt$. By the

fundamental theorem of calculus, $f_x = -\ln(\cos\sqrt{x})$

and $f_y = \ln(\cos\sqrt{y})$.

47. $u = e^{ax}\cos ay$. Note that $u_x = ae^{ax}\cos ay$,

$u_{xx} = a^2 e^{ax}\cos ay$, $u_y = -ae^{ax}\sin ay$, and $u_{yy} = -a^2 e^{ax}\cos ay$.

This shows $u_{xx} + u_{yy} = 0$, so u is harmonic.

[See exercise set 3, problems 57 and 58.]

51. $u = f(x,y,z) = ze^{xy}$

$du = f_x dx + f_y dy + f_z dz = e^{xy}(yz\ dx + xz\ dy + dz)$

55. $u = xy + yz - zx$; $x = r + s$, $y = rs$, $z = s$

$\dfrac{\partial u}{\partial r} = \dfrac{\partial u}{\partial x}\dfrac{\partial x}{\partial r} + \dfrac{\partial u}{\partial y}\dfrac{\partial y}{\partial r} + \dfrac{\partial u}{\partial z}\dfrac{\partial z}{\partial r}$

$\quad = (y-z) + (x+z)(s) + (y-x)(0)$

$\quad = rs - s + (r+2s)s = 2rs - s + 2s^2$

$\dfrac{\partial u}{\partial s} = \dfrac{\partial u}{\partial x}\dfrac{\partial x}{\partial s} + \dfrac{\partial u}{\partial y}\dfrac{\partial y}{\partial s} + \dfrac{\partial u}{\partial z}\dfrac{\partial z}{\partial s} = (y-z)(1) + (x+z)(r) + (y-x)(1)$

$\quad = rs - s + (r+2s)r + rs - r - s = 4rs + r^2 - r - 2s$

59. $f(x,y,z) = x^{(y^z)}$

$df = f_x dx + f_y dy + f_z dz$

$$= y^z x^{(y^z-1)} dx + (\ln x)(zy^{z-1})(x^{(y^z)}) dy$$

$$+ (\ln x)(\ln y)(y^z)(x^{(y^z)}) dz$$

$g(x,y,z) = (x^y)^z = x^{yz}$

$dg = g_x dx + g_y dy + g_z dz = yz(x^{yz-1}) dx + z \ln(x)(x^{yz}) dy$

$$+ y \ln(x)(x^{yz}) dz$$

Chapter Seventeen

Exercise 1, pp. 923-925

3. $f(x,y) = 2xy - y^2$; $f_x = 2y$; $f_y = 2x - 2y$

   $f_x(-1,3) = 2(3) = 6$; $f_y(-1,3) = 2(-1) - 2(3) = -8$

   $D_{\vec{u}}f(-1,3) = 6 \cos \frac{2\pi}{3} - 8 \sin \frac{2\pi}{3} = -3 - 8 \frac{\sqrt{3}}{2} = -3 - 4\sqrt{3}$

7. $f(x,y) = \tan^{-1}(\frac{y}{x})$; $f_x = \frac{-y}{x^2 + y^2}$; $f_y = \frac{x}{x^2 + y^2}$

   $f_x(1,1) = -\frac{1}{2}$; $f_y(1,1) = \frac{1}{2}$; $\vec{u} = \frac{1}{5}(3\vec{i} - 4\vec{j})$

   $D_{\vec{u}}f(1,1) = (-\frac{1}{2})(\frac{3}{5}) + \frac{1}{2}(\frac{-4}{5}) = -\frac{7}{10}$

11. $f(x,y,z) = xe^{yz}$; $f_x = e^{yz}$; $f_y = xze^{yz}$; $f_z = xye^{yz}$

   $f_x(1,0,1) = e^0 = 1$; $f_y(1,0,1) = e^0 = 1$; $f_z(1,0,1) = 0$

   $\vec{u} = \frac{1}{\|\vec{a}\|}(2\vec{i} + \vec{j}) = \frac{\sqrt{5}}{5}(2\vec{i} + \vec{j})$

   $D_{\vec{u}}f(1,0,1) = \vec{\nabla}f \cdot \vec{u} = \frac{\sqrt{5}}{5}(2 + 1) = \frac{3\sqrt{5}}{5}$

15. $f(x,y) = \tan^{-1}(\frac{y}{x}) \Rightarrow \vec{\nabla}f = \frac{1}{1 + (\frac{y}{x})^2}(\frac{-y}{x^2})\vec{i} + \frac{1}{1 + (\frac{y}{x})^2}(\frac{1}{x})\vec{j}$

   $= \frac{-y}{x^2 + y^2}\vec{i} + \frac{x}{x^2 + y^2}\vec{j}$

19. $f(x,y,z) = xe^{yz}$

   $\Rightarrow \vec{\nabla}f = e^{yz}\vec{i} + xze^{yz}\vec{j} + xye^{yz}\vec{k}$

   $\Rightarrow \vec{\nabla}f\Big|_{P = (1,0,1)} = e^0\vec{i} + 1\cdot 1e^0\vec{j} + 1\cdot 0e^0\vec{k}$

   $= \vec{i} + \vec{j}$

23. $z = f(x,y) = xe^y + ye^x$; $f_x = e^y + ye^x$;

$f_y = xe^y + e^x$; $f_x(0,0) = 1$; $f_y(0,0) = 1$

Hence, the direction is that of the unit vector $(\vec{i} + \vec{j})/\sqrt{2}$.
Rate of increase is $\sqrt{1^2 + 1^2} = \sqrt{2}$.

27. $f(x,y) = x^2 + y^2 \Rightarrow \vec{\nabla}f = 2x\vec{i} + 2y\vec{j}$

$f(3,4) = 25 \Rightarrow$ Level curve is $x^2 + y^2 = 25$

$\vec{\nabla}f\bigg|_{P = (3,4)} = 6\vec{i} + 8\vec{j}$

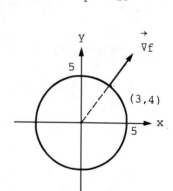

31. $f(x,y) = x^2y \Rightarrow \vec{\nabla}f = 2xy\vec{i} + x^2\vec{j}$

$f(3, \frac{1}{9}) = 1 \Rightarrow$ Level curve is $x^2y = 1$ or $y = \frac{1}{x^2}$

$\vec{\nabla}f\bigg|_{P = (3,\frac{1}{9})} = \frac{2}{3}\vec{i} + 9\vec{j}$

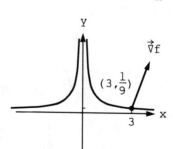

35. $V(x,y) = \ln\sqrt{x^2 + y^2} = \frac{1}{2}\ln(x^2+y^2)$;

$V_x(x,y) = \frac{x}{x^2+y^2}$; $V_y(x,y) = \frac{y}{x^2+y^2}$

(a) From (x, y), a unit vector toward $(0, 0)$ is given by

$\dfrac{-x\vec{i} - y\vec{j}}{\sqrt{x^2+y^2}}$. Forming the dot product of this vector

with $\vec{\nabla}V(x, y)$, we find the rate of change in the

direction of $(0, 0)$ is $\dfrac{-x^2-y^2}{(x^2+y^2)^{3/2}} = -(x^2+y^2)^{1/2}$

(b) Unit vectors in these two directions are

$(y\vec{i}-x\vec{j})/\sqrt{x^2+y^2}$ and $(-y\vec{i}+x\vec{j})/\sqrt{x^2+y^2}$. Dotting these

vectors with $\vec{\nabla}V(x,y)$, we obtain 0 as the rate of

change in each case.

(c) It is maximum in the direction of $\vec{\nabla}V(x, y)$, namely

the direction $x\vec{i}+y\vec{j}$, away from the origin.

(d) It is minimum in the direction $-x\vec{i}-y\vec{j}$, toward the

origin.

39. $z = f(x, y) = xy^2$; $f_x = y^2$; $f_y = 2xy$

$f_x = (-1, 1) = 1$; $f_y(-1, 1) = -2$

We seek θ such that $\vec{\nabla}f(-1, 1)\cdot[\cos\theta\vec{i} + \sin\theta\vec{j}] = 2$,

or $\cos\theta - 2\sin\theta = 2$. To solve this, we transpose

and square:

$\cos^2\theta = 4(1 + \sin\theta)^2$

$1-\sin^2\theta = 4 + 8\sin\theta + 4\sin^2\theta$

$5\sin^2\theta + 8\sin\theta + 3 = 0$

$(5\sin\theta + 3)(\sin\theta + 1) = 0 \Rightarrow \sin\theta = -1, -3/5$

Since $\cos\theta = 2(1+\sin\theta)$, the respective values of

$\cos\theta$ are 0, 4/5. Directions are thus $-j$ and $\dfrac{4}{5}\vec{i} - \dfrac{3}{5}\vec{j}$.

43. $f(x, y) = 2x^2 + y^2 + 1 \Rightarrow \vec{\nabla}f = 4x\vec{i} + 2y\vec{j}$

By Theorem (17.11), $\vec{\nabla}f\bigg|_{P = (1, 1)} = 4\vec{i} + 2\vec{j}$

is perpendicular to the level curve of f through

P = (1, 1). The required unit vector is:

$$\vec{u} = \frac{4\vec{i} + 2\vec{j}}{\|4\vec{i} + 2\vec{j}\|} = \frac{4\vec{i} + 2\vec{j}}{\sqrt{20}} = \frac{2\vec{i} + \vec{j}}{\sqrt{5}}.$$

Exercise 2, pp. 927-928

3. $F(x,y,z) = 2x^2 + 3y^2 - z^2 - 10$

$F_x = 4x; \quad F_y = 6y; \quad F_z = -2z$

$\vec{\nabla}F(2,1,-1) = 8\vec{i} + 6\vec{j} + 2\vec{k}$

Tangent plane: $8(x-2) + 6(y-1) + 2(z+1) = 0$

or $4x + 3y + z = 10$

Normal line: $\dfrac{x - 2}{8} = \dfrac{y - 1}{6} = \dfrac{z + 1}{2}$

7. $F(x,y,z) = x^2 + y^2 - z$

$F_x = 2x; \quad F_y = 2y; \quad F_z = -1$

$\vec{\nabla}F(-2,1,5) = -4\vec{i} + 2\vec{j} - \vec{k}$

Tangent plane: $-4(x+2) + 2(y-1) - (z-5) = 0$

or $4x - 2y + z = -5$

Normal line: $\dfrac{x + 2}{-4} = \dfrac{y - 1}{2} = \dfrac{z - 5}{-1}$

11. $F(x,y,z) = e^x \cos y - z$

$F_x = e^x \cos y; \quad F_y = -e^x \sin y; \quad F_z = -1$

$\vec{\nabla}F(0, \dfrac{\pi}{2}, 0) = -\vec{j} - \vec{k}$

Tangent plane: $-(y - \dfrac{\pi}{2}) - (z - 0) = 0$ or $y + z = \dfrac{\pi}{2}$

Normal line: $z = y - \dfrac{\pi}{2}, \quad x = 0$

15. $F(x,y,z) = 6x - 4y - x^2 - 2y^2 - z$

$\vec{\nabla}F = (6-2x)\vec{i} + (-4 - 4y)\vec{j} - \vec{k}$

This is parallel to the z-axis when $6 - 2x = 4 + 4y$ $= 0$, or $x = 3$, $y = -1$. The point on the surface is $(3,-1,11)$.

19. $F(x,y,z) = 2x^4 - y^2 - x^2 - 2y - z$

$\vec{\nabla}F = (8x^3-2x)\vec{i} + (-2y-2)\vec{j} - \vec{k}$

This is parallel to the z-axis when $8x^3 - 2x$ $= 2y + 2 = 0$ or $y = -1$, $2x(4x^2-1) = 0$. The points on the surface are $(0,-1,1)$, $(\pm\frac{1}{2}, -1, \frac{7}{8})$.

23. Let $F(x,y,z) = x^2 + y^2 + z^2 - a^2$, $\vec{\nabla}F = (2x)\vec{i} + (2y)\vec{j} + (2z)\vec{k}$. Hence, the normal vector at a point (x_0,y_0,z_0) on the sphere is given by $\vec{\nabla}F(x_0,y_0,z_0)$ $= 2x_0\vec{i} + 2y_0\vec{j} + 2z_0\vec{k}$. Symmetric equations for the normal line: $x = x_0 + 2x_0t$, $y = y_0 + 2y_0t$, $z = z_0 + 2z_0t$. This line passes through the origin (the center of the sphere) for $t = \frac{-1}{2}$.

27. $F(x,y,z) = x \sin(yz) - 1$

$\Rightarrow \vec{\nabla}F = \sin(yz)\vec{i} + xz \cos(yz)\vec{j} + xy \cos(yz)\vec{k}$

$\Rightarrow \vec{\nabla}F\Big|_{P_0 = (1,1,\frac{\pi}{2})} = 1\vec{i} + \frac{\pi}{2}(0)\vec{j} + 1(0)\vec{k} = \vec{i}$

$G(x,y,z) = ze^{y^2-x^2} - \frac{\pi}{2}$

$\Rightarrow \vec{\nabla}G = -2xze^{y^2-x^2}\vec{i} + 2yze^{y^2-x^2}\vec{j} + e^{y^2-x^2}\vec{k}$

$\Rightarrow \vec{\nabla}G\Big|_{P_0 = (1,1,\frac{\pi}{2})} = -2(1)(\frac{\pi}{2})e^0\vec{i} + 2(1)(\frac{\pi}{2})e^0\vec{j} + e^0\vec{k}$

$= -\pi\vec{i} + \pi\vec{j} + \vec{k}$

A line tangent to the intersection of the curves, must be perpendicular to the normal line for each curve at the point of intersection. We want a vector $\vec{v} = a\vec{i} + b\vec{j} + c\vec{k}$ such that $\vec{v} \cdot \vec{\nabla}F(1,1,\frac{\pi}{2}) = 0$

and $\vec{v} \cdot \vec{\nabla}G(1,1,\frac{\pi}{2}) = 0$. $\vec{v} = \vec{j} - \pi\vec{k}$ is one such vector.

Then the equations for the tangent line through the

point $(1,1,\frac{\pi}{2})$ are $x = 1 + (0)t$, $y = 1 + (1)t$,

$z = \frac{\pi}{2} - (\pi)t$ or, simply, $x = 1$, $z = \frac{3\pi}{2} - \pi y$.

Exercise 3, pp. 935-937

3. $f(x,y) = 4xy - x^4 - y^4 + 2$

$f_x = 4y - 4x^3 = 0 \Rightarrow y = x^3$

$f_y = 4x - 4y^3 = 0 \Rightarrow x = y^3$

Substituting the second equation in the first yields:

$y = (y^3)^3$ or $y = y^9$

which is true only for the real values of $y = 0$,

$y = 1$, and $y = -1$.

Critical points: $(0,0)$, $(1,1)$, $(-1,-1)$

7. $f(x,y) = x^2 + y^2 - 2x + 4y + 2$

$f_x = 2x - 2 = 0 \Rightarrow x = 1$

$f_y = 2y + 4 = 0 \Rightarrow y = -2$

$f_{xx} = 2$, $f_{yy} = 2$, $f_{xy} = 0$

$f_{xx}f_{yy} - f_{xy}^2 = 4 > 0$ and $f_{xx} > 0$

$\Rightarrow$ local minimum at $(1,-2)$

11. $f(x,y) = x^3 - 6xy + y^3$

$f_x = 3x^2 - 6y = 0 \Rightarrow x^2 = 2y$

$f_y = -6x + 3y^2 = 0 \Rightarrow y^2 = 2x$

Substituting the first equation into the second yields:

$(\frac{x^2}{2})^2 = 2x \Rightarrow x^4 - 8x = 0$

$\Rightarrow x(x^3-8) = 0 \Rightarrow x = 0$ or $x = 2$

384   CHAPTER SEVENTEEN

Using $\frac{x^2}{2} = y$. we have the critical points $(0,0)$ and $(2,2)$.

$f_{xx} = 6x$, $f_{yy} = 6y$, $f_{xy} = -6$

For $(0,0)$:

$f_{xx}f_{yy} - f_{xy}^2 = -36 < 0 \Rightarrow$ saddle point at $(0,0)$

For $(2,2)$

$f_{xx}f_{yy} - f_{xy}^2 = (12)(12) - (36) = 108 > 0$, $f_{xx} = 12 > 0$

$\Rightarrow$ local minimum at $(2,2)$

15. $f(x,y) = x^3 + 3xy + y^3$

$f_x = 3x^2 + 3y = 0 \Rightarrow y = -x^2$

$f_y = 3x + 3y^2 = 0 \Rightarrow x = -y^2$

Substituting the second equation in the first yields:

$y = - (-y^2)^2 \Rightarrow y = -y^4 \Rightarrow y(y^3+1) = 0$

$\Rightarrow y = 0$ or $y = -1$.

Using $x = -y^2$ we have the two critical points $(0,0)$

and $(-1,-1)$.

$f_{xx} = 6x$, $f_{yy} = 6y$, $f_{xy} = 3$

For $(0,0)$:

$f_{xx}f_{yy} - f_{xy}^2 = -9 < 0 \Rightarrow$ saddle point at $(0,0)$

For $(-1,-1)$:

$f_{xx}f_{yy} - f_{xy}^2 = (-6)(-6) - (3)^2 = 27 > 0$ and $f_{xx} = -6 < 0$

$\Rightarrow$ local maximum at $(-1,-1)$

19. $f(x,y) = \dfrac{y}{x + y}$

$f_x = \dfrac{-y}{(x+y)^2} = 0$

$f_y = \dfrac{x}{(x+y)^2} = 0$

This yields only $(0,0)$ as a possible critical point, but f is not even defined at that point. Therefore, no local extrema.

23. $f(x,y) = y^2 - 6y \cos x + 6$

$f_x = 6 y \sin x = 0 \Rightarrow y \sin x = 0$

$f_y = 2y - 6 \cos x = 0 \Rightarrow y = 3 \cos x$

Substituting the second equation in the first yields:

$3 \cos x \sin x = 0 \Rightarrow \frac{3}{2} \sin 2x = 0 \Rightarrow x = n\pi/2$,

for n any integer.

From $y = 3 \cos x$ we have the following critical points:

$((2n+1)\frac{\pi}{2},0)$, $(2n\pi,3)$, $((2n+1)\pi,-3)$,

where n is any integer.

$f_{xx} = 6 y \cos x$, $f_{yy} = 2$, $f_{xy} = 6 \sin x$

$f_{xx}f_{yy} - f_{xy}^2 = 12 y \cos x - 36 \sin^2 x$

For $((2n+1)\frac{\pi}{2},0)$, $12 y \cos x - 36 \sin^2 x = -36 < 0$

$\Rightarrow$ saddle points.

For $(2n\pi,3)$, $12 y \cos x - 36 \sin^2 x = 36 > 0$

and $f_{xx} = 18 > 0 \Rightarrow$ local minima.

For $((2n+1)\pi,-3)$, $12 y \cos x - 36 \sin^2 x = 36 > 0$

and $f_{xx} = 18 > 0 \Rightarrow$ local minima.

27. $z = f(x,y) = -(x^2-6x+y^2+4y+12)$

(a) Completing the square on both x and y, we find

$z = -(x^2-6x+9) - (y^2+4y+4) + 1$, or $z = 1-(x-3)^2-(y+2)^2$.

This reveals the vertex to be $(3,-2,1)$.

(b) $f_x = -2x+6 = 0$; $f_y = -2y-4 = 0$. Solving gives a

critical point at $(3,-2)$. Now $f_{xx}(3,-2) = -2$,

$f_{xy}(3,-2) = 0$, and $f_{yy}(3,-2) = -2$. Since $AC-B^2$

$= 4 > 0$, with $A < 0$, (17.23) shows that $(3,-2,1)$

is a local maximum.

31. Let x = length, y = width, and z = depth. Surface area

$S = 2(xy+xz+yz)$. Solving for z, $z = (\frac{1}{2}S - xy)/(x+y)$.

Hence, volume $V = xyz = \frac{xy}{x+y}(\frac{1}{2}S - xy)$.

Now, $V_x = \frac{-xy^2}{x+y} + (\frac{1}{2}S - xy)(y^2/(x+y)^2) = 0$ and

$V_y = \frac{-x^2y}{x+y} + (\frac{1}{2}S - xy)(x^2/(x+y)^2) = 0$. Multiplying

these by $(x+y)^2$, we find $(\frac{1}{2}S - xy)(y^2)-x^2y^2-xy^3 = 0$

and $(\frac{1}{2}S - xy)(x^2)-x^2y^2-yx^3 = 0$ or $S = 4xy+2x^2 = 4xy+2y^2$.

This gives $x = y = \sqrt{S/6}$. Since $z = (\frac{1}{2}S - xy)/(x+y)$,

$z = [(S/2)-(S/6)]/2\sqrt{S/6} = \sqrt{S/6}$. Hence, $x = y = z = \sqrt{S/6}$.

Calculating the second partial derivatives, we find

$V_{xx} = \frac{-2y^2}{(x+y)^3}(\frac{1}{2}S + y^2)$, $V_{yy} = \frac{-2x^2}{(x+y)^3}(\frac{1}{2}S + x^2)$, and

$V_{xy} = \frac{2}{(x+y)^3}(\frac{1}{2}Sxy - x^3y - 3x^2y^2 - xy^3)$. Evaluating

these at $x = y = \sqrt{S/6}$, $V_{xx} = V_{yy} = \frac{-1}{4\sqrt{S/6}}(\frac{2}{3}S) = -\sqrt{S/6}$

and $V_{xy} = \frac{1}{4(S/6)\sqrt{S/6}}\left[\frac{S^2}{12} - \frac{5S^2}{36}\right] = -\frac{1}{2}\sqrt{\frac{S}{6}}$.

Hence, $V_{xx}V_{yy}-(V_{xy})^2 = \frac{S}{6} - \frac{S}{24} = \frac{S}{8} > 0$, with

$V_{xx} = -\sqrt{S/6} < 0$. Thus, we have a maximum at $x = y = z$

$= \sqrt{S/6}$.

35. Since the flow is proportional to the cross-sectional area, we will maximize

$A = (L-2x)h + 2 \cdot \frac{1}{2}h(x \sin\theta)$

$A = x(L-2x)\cos\theta + x^2 \sin\theta \cos\theta$

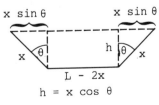

$h = x \cos \theta$

A_x = (L-4x)cos θ + 2x sin θ cos θ = cos θ [(L-4x) + 2x sin θ]

A_θ = -(L-2x)x sin θ + x^2 ($\cos^2\theta - \sin^2\theta$)

Set A_x = 0 and since cos θ ≠ 0 (i.e. θ ≠ 90°), we have

(L-4x) + 2x sin θ = 0 or sin θ = $\dfrac{4x - L}{2x}$.

Substituting this value into A_θ and using the relationship

$\cos^2\theta - \sin^2\theta$ = $(1-\sin^2\theta) - \sin^2\theta$ = $1 - 2\sin^2\theta$ we have

A_θ = $-3x^2$ + xL = x(-3x+L).

Since A_θ = 0 and x ≠ 0 we must have X = $\dfrac{L}{3}$ and thus

from sin θ = $\dfrac{4x - L}{2x}$, we have sin θ = $\dfrac{1}{2}$ or θ = 30° (and

therefore, h = x cos θ = $\dfrac{L}{2\sqrt{3}}$). $A_{xx}A_{\theta\theta} - A_{x\theta} > 0$ and A_{xx}

< 0, thus we have a local (actually, absolute) maximum.

The maximum cross-sectional area is $A(\frac{L}{3}, 30°)$ = $\dfrac{\sqrt{3}L^2}{12}$.

Semicircular area = L^2/π, which is larger.

39. C = $\dfrac{1}{20}x^2$ + 700x + y^2 - 150y - $\dfrac{1}{2}xy$

R = 2700 x - $\dfrac{3}{20}x^2$ + 1000y - y^2 + $\dfrac{1}{2}xy$ + 10,000

Maximize P = R - C

P_x = 2700 - $\dfrac{3}{10}x$ + $\dfrac{1}{2}y$ - $\dfrac{1}{10}x$ - 700 + $\dfrac{1}{2}y$

  = 2000 + y - $\dfrac{2}{5}x$ = 0

P_y = 1000 - 2y + $\dfrac{1}{2}x$ - 2y + 150 + $\dfrac{1}{2}x$

  = 1150 + x - 4y = 0

Solving these two equations simultaneously yields:

x = 15250 and y = 4100

$P_{xx} = \dfrac{-2}{5}$, $P_{yy} = -4$, $P_{xy} = 1$

$P_{xx}P_{yy} - P_{xy}^2 = \dfrac{8}{5} - 1 = \dfrac{3}{5} > 0$ and $P_{xx} < 0$

=> local maximum when $x = 15250$ and $y = 4100$

Exercise 4, pp. 944-945

3. $f(x,y) = x^2 + 4y^3$, $g(x,y) = x^2 + 2y^2 - 2 = 0$.
   $\vec{\nabla}f = \lambda\vec{\nabla}g$, or $2x\vec{i} + 12y^2\vec{j} = \lambda(2x\vec{i} + 4y\vec{j})$. This
   gives $2x = 2x\lambda$, $12y^2 = 4y\lambda$, $x^2 + 2y^2 = 2$. If
   $x = 0$, $y = \pm1$ by the third equation. If $x \neq 0$,
   the first equation gives $\lambda = 1$, so $y = 0$ or
   $\dfrac{1}{3}$ from the second equation, and in turn (x,y)
   $= (\pm\sqrt{2},0)$ or $(\pm\dfrac{4}{3}, \dfrac{1}{3})$. Computing f at the six
   points found, $f(0,1) = 4$, $f(0,-1) = -4$,
   $f(\pm\sqrt{2},0) = 2$, and $f(\pm\dfrac{4}{3}, \dfrac{1}{3}) = \dfrac{52}{27}$. This shows
   f has a maximum of 4 at $(0,1)$ and a minimum of
   -4 at $(0,-1)$.

7. $f(x,y,z) = 4x - 3y + 2z$, $g(x,y,z) = x^2 + y^2 - 6z = 0$.
   $\vec{\nabla}f = \lambda\vec{\nabla}g$, or $4\vec{i} - 3\vec{j} + 2\vec{k} = \lambda(2x\vec{i} + 2y\vec{j} - 6\vec{k})$. This
   gives $4 = 2x\lambda$, $-3 = 2y\lambda$, $2 = -6\lambda$, $x^2 + y^2 = 6z$.
   Immediately these give $\lambda = -\dfrac{1}{3}$, $x = -6$, $y = \dfrac{9}{2}$,
   and $z = \dfrac{1}{6}(36 + \dfrac{81}{4})$. The only critical point for
   f is thus $(-6, \dfrac{9}{2}, \dfrac{225}{24})$. The value of f here
   is $-24 - \dfrac{27}{2} + \dfrac{225}{12} = -\dfrac{225}{12}$. This is a *minimum*,
   since, for example, we may compute $f(0,0,0) = 0$.

11. Maximize $f(x,y) = xy$, with constraint $g(x,y)$
    $= x^2 + 2y^2 - 2 = 0$. $\vec{\nabla}f = \lambda\vec{\nabla}g$, or $y\vec{i} + x\vec{j}$

$= \lambda[2x\vec{i} + 4y\vec{j}]$. This gives $y = 2\lambda x$, $x = 4\lambda y$, $x^2 + 2y^2 = 2$. Since x cannot be 0 (or y would be 0 and the third equation would fail), $x = 4(\frac{y}{2x})y$ or $x^2 = 2y^2$. This and the third equation yield $x = \pm 1$, $y = \pm \frac{\sqrt{2}}{2}$. Since $f(x,y) = xy$, we see that f has a maximum of $\frac{\sqrt{2}}{2}$ at $(1, \frac{\sqrt{2}}{2})$ and $(-1, -\frac{\sqrt{2}}{2})$.

15. (a) If the rectangular field has width x, its length is $2x$. Let y be the width of the square field. We have $2x^2 \geq 800$ and $y^2 \geq 100$, or $x \geq 20$ and $y \geq 10$. Since $6x + 4y = 340$, $6x \leq 300$ or $x \leq 50$. Hence, $20 \leq x \leq 50$. Maximum $x = 50$ m, minimum $x = 20$ m. (Note: This is all assuming the fields do not have a side in common. If they do, though, x is forced to take on a specific value between 20 and 50.)

(b) If the fields have no side in common, we maximize $2x^2 + y^2$ subject to the constraint $6x + 4y = 340$. Then $y = \frac{1}{4}(340-6x)$ and area $A(x) = 2x^2 + \frac{1}{16}(340-6x)^2 = 2x^2 + \frac{9}{4}x^2 - 255x + \frac{1}{16}(340)^2$. Set $A'(x) = \frac{17}{2}x - 255 = 0$, so

$x = 30$ m, thus $y = 40$ m and area $= 1800 + 1600 = 3400$ m^2.

One can do even better, though, if the long side of the rectangle can be used as one side of the square. We then have: Perimeter $= 12x = 340$, so $x = \frac{85}{3}$; Area $= 6x^2 = 6(\frac{85}{3})^2 \approx 4817$ m^2

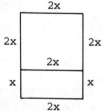

(The alternative of using x as a common side results in an area ≈ 4281 m^2.)

3. $V = V(x, y, z) = e^{xyz}$; $\vec{\nabla}V = e^{xyz}(yz\vec{i}+xz\vec{j}+xy\vec{k})$

   $\vec{\nabla}V(1, -1, 2) = e^{-2}(-2\vec{i}+2\vec{j}-\vec{k})$

   Direction of greatest potential <u>drop</u> is thus

   $2\vec{i}-2\vec{j}+\vec{k}$, and rate is $\|\vec{\nabla}(1, -1, 2)\| = 3e^{-2}$.

7. Let $\vec{R}(t) = x(t)\vec{i} + y(t)\vec{j}$ be a smooth parametrization of

   the curve $F(x,y) = 0$. We know $\dfrac{d\vec{R}}{dt}$ is a tangent vector to the

   curve at any point. Since this tangent vector is normal

   to $\vec{\nabla} = F_x\vec{i} + F_y\vec{j}$, it must be a multiple of $F_y\vec{i} - F_x\vec{j}$, as the

   dot product of these two vectors is zero. At (x_0, y_0), the

   tangent to $F(x, y) = 0$ thus has slope

   $-F_x(x_0, y_0)/F_y(x_0,y_0) = -\dfrac{a}{b}$, so its equation is

   $y-y_0 = (-\dfrac{a}{b})(x-x_0)$, or $a(x-x_0)+b(y-y_0) = 0$.

11. We consider L_1 as given by $\{(s-6, s, 2s): s \text{ real}\}$

   and L_2 by $\{(t, t, -t): t \text{ real}\}$. We seek to minimize

   $f(s, t) = [(s-6)-t]^2+(s-t)^2+(2s+t)^2 = 6s^2-12s+12t$

   $+3t^2+36$. Set $f_s = 12s-12 = 0$ and $f_t = 6t+12 = 0$.

   This gives $s=1$, $t = -2$. $f_{ss}=12$, $f_{tt}=6$, $f_{st}=0$ =>

   $f_{ss}f_{tt} - f_{st}^2 > 0$ and $f_{ss} > 0$ => local minimum at

   $(s, t) = (1, -2)$ and $f(1, -2) = (-5+2)^2+3^2+0^2 = 18$.

   The minimum distance is then $\sqrt{18} = 3\sqrt{2}$.

15. Let the dimensions be x, y, and z. We wish to

   maximize $V(x, y, z) = xyz$, subject to the constraint

$S(x, y, z) = 2(xy+xz+yz) = S_0$. Write $\vec{\nabla}V = \lambda \vec{\nabla}S$,

giving (1) $yz = 2\lambda(y+z)$; (2) $xz = 2\lambda(x+z)$;

(3) $xy = 2\lambda(x+y)$. As $\lambda = 0$ is clearly impossible

(volume would then be 0), these equations give

$\dfrac{yz}{y+z} = \dfrac{xz}{x+z} = \dfrac{xy}{x+y}$. From $\dfrac{yz}{y+z} = \dfrac{xz}{x+z}$ we have $xy + zy = xy + zx$,

since each dimension must be non-zero. Hence $y = x$.

Similarly from the second equality we can obtain $y = z$.

This shows $x = y = z$, so we have a cube.

19. Set $F(x, y, z) = \sin(x+y) + \sin(y+z)-1 = 0$. Now

$\vec{\nabla}F = \cos(x+y)\vec{i} + [\cos(x+y)+\cos(y+z)]\vec{j} + \cos(y+z)\vec{k}$,

so by (17.18) the tangent plane has equation

$(\cos \frac{\pi}{2})(x-0)+[\cos \frac{\pi}{2} + \cos\pi](y - \frac{\pi}{2})+(\cos\pi)(z - \frac{\pi}{2}) = 0$,

or $-(y - \frac{\pi}{2}) - (z - \frac{\pi}{2}) = 0$, or $y+z = \pi$. The normal

line has equations $x=0, \dfrac{y - \pi/2}{-1} = \dfrac{z - \pi/2}{-1}$, or $x=0$, $y=z$.

23. $T = \sqrt{9-x^2-y^2-z^2}$

$\vec{\nabla}T = \dfrac{-x}{\sqrt{9-x^2-y^2-z^2}}\vec{i} + \dfrac{-y}{\sqrt{9-x^2-y^2-z^2}}\vec{j} + \dfrac{-z}{\sqrt{9-x^2-y^2-z^2}}\vec{k}$

The unit vector in the direction from $(0, 1, 2)$ to

$(2, 1, 2)$ is $\vec{i}$.

$D_{\vec{i}}f = \vec{\nabla}T \cdot \vec{i} = \dfrac{-x}{\sqrt{9-x^2-y^2-z^2}}$ and $D_{\vec{i}}f(x, 1, 2) = \dfrac{-x}{\sqrt{4-x^2}}$

$T(0, 1, 2) = 2$ and $T(2, 1, 2) = 0$. At $(0, 1, 2)$,

$D_{\vec{i}}f = 0$, i.e. no change in T in the $\vec{i}$ direction.

However, as we move x from 0 to 2, $D_{\vec{i}}f \to -\infty$. Thus,

Thus, as we move from $(0, 1, 2)$ to $(2, 1, 2)$, T decreases more and more rapidly until $T = 0$ at $(2, 1, 2)$.

27. $f(x,y,z) = z^3 + 3xz - y^2$. Note that $f_x = 3z$, $f_y = -2y$, $f_z = 3z^2 + 3x$. Hence, $f_x(1,2,1) = 3$, $f_y(1,2,1) = -4$, and $f_z(1,2,1) = 6$. Now unit vectors in the direction of the line given are $\vec{u} = \pm \frac{\sqrt{3}}{3}(\vec{i} + \vec{j} + \vec{k})$. The directional derivatives sought are thus $\vec{\nabla}f(1,2,1) \cdot \vec{u} = \pm \frac{\sqrt{3}}{3}(3-4+6) = \pm \frac{5\sqrt{3}}{3}$.

Chapter Eighteen

Exercise 1, pp. 953-954

3. $f(x,y) = 2xy - y^2$; $x_0 = 0$, $x_1 = 2$, $x_2 = 4$, $y_0 = 0$,
$y_1 = 1$, $y_2 = 2$

$$\sum_{i=1}^{4} f(u_i, v_i)\Delta A_i = f(0,0)\Delta A_1 + f(2,0)\Delta A_2 + f(0,1)\Delta A_3$$

$$+ f(2,1)\Delta A_4 = 0(2) + 0(2) + (-1)(2) + (4-1)(2)$$
$$= -2 + 6 = 4$$

7. Set $\iint_R f(x,y)\,dA = \alpha$, $\iint_{R_1} f(x,y)\,dA = \alpha_1$, and

and $\iint_{R_2} f(x,y)\,dA = \alpha_2$. We are given that

(1) $3\alpha = 2\alpha_1 + \alpha_2$, (2) $5\alpha_2 - 2\alpha_1 = 18$. Also, it is
always true, by (18.9), that (3) $\alpha = \alpha_1 + \alpha_2$.
Combining (1) and (3), $3\alpha_1 + 3\alpha_2 = 2\alpha_1 + \alpha_2$, or
$\alpha_1 = -2\alpha_2$. Substituting the latter in (2), $9\alpha_2 = 18$.
Hence, $\alpha_2 = 2$, $\alpha_1 = -4$, so $\alpha = \iint_R f(x,y)\,dA = -2$.

Exercise 2, pp. 960-961

3. $\displaystyle\int_{-1}^{2} \left[\int_{y^2}^{y+2} dx \right] dy$

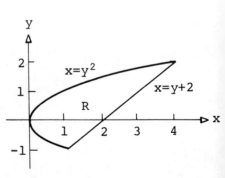

$$= \int_{-1}^{2} (y+2-y^2)\,dy$$

$$= \left(\frac{1}{2} y^2 + 2y - \frac{1}{3} y^3\right)\Big|_{-1}^{2}$$

$$= [\tfrac{1}{2}(4) + 4 - \tfrac{8}{3}] - [\tfrac{1}{2}(1) - 2 + \tfrac{1}{3}]$$

$$= \frac{10}{3} + \frac{7}{6} = \frac{9}{2}$$

7. $\int_0^2 \left[\int_y^{2y} xy\ dx \right] dy$

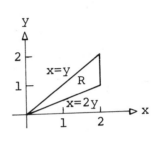

$$= \int_0^2 \left[y\ \frac{x^2}{2}\Big|_y^{2y} \right] dy$$

$$= \int_0^2 y(2y^2 - \frac{y^2}{2})\,dy$$

$$= (\frac{y^4}{2} - \frac{y^4}{8})\Big|_0^2 = 8 - 2 = 6$$

11.

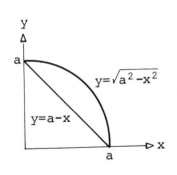

$\int_0^a \left[\int_{a-x}^{\sqrt{a^2-x^2}} y\ dy \right] dx$

$$= \int_0^a \left[\frac{y^2}{2}\Big|_{a-x}^{\sqrt{a^2-x^2}} \right] dx$$

$$= \frac{1}{2} \int_0^a [a^2 - x^2 - (a-x)^2]\,dx$$

$$= \frac{1}{2} \int_0^a (2ax - 2x^2)\,dx$$

$$= (a\,\frac{x^2}{2} - \frac{x^3}{3})\Big|_0^a = \frac{a^3}{6}$$

15. $\int\limits_{0}^{2} \left[\int\limits_{0}^{\ell nx} xe^y dy \right] dx$

$= \int\limits_{1}^{2} x \left[e^y \Big|_{0}^{\ell nx} \right] dx$

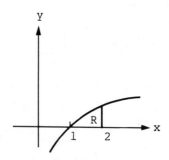

$= \int\limits_{1}^{2} x(x-1)dx = \int\limits_{1}^{2} (x^2-x)dx = (\frac{x^3}{3} - \frac{x^2}{2}) \Big|_{1}^{2}$

$= (\frac{8}{3} - 2) - (\frac{1}{3} - \frac{1}{2}) = \frac{5}{6}$

19.

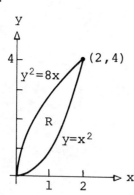

$\int\int_R (x+y)dA$

$= \int\limits_{0}^{2} \left[\int\limits_{x^2}^{\sqrt{8x}} (x+y)dy \right] dx$

$= \int\limits_{0}^{2} [(xy + \frac{y^2}{2})|_{x^2}^{\sqrt{8x}}]dx$

$= \int\limits_{0}^{2} (\sqrt{8}x^{3/2} + 8(\frac{x}{2}) - x^3 - \frac{x^4}{2})dx$

$= (\sqrt{8} \frac{2}{5} x^{5/2} + 2x^2 - \frac{x^4}{4} - \frac{x^5}{10}) \Big|_{0}^{2}$

$= \frac{2}{5}(16) + 8 - 4 - \frac{32}{10} = \frac{36}{5}$

23.

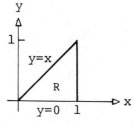

$\int\limits_{0}^{1} [\int\limits_{0}^{x} f(x,y)dy]dx$

$= \int\limits_{0}^{1} [\int\limits_{y}^{1} f(x,y)dx]dy$

27.

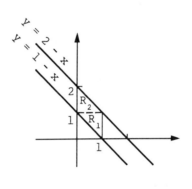

$$x = 2y \Rightarrow y = \tfrac{1}{2}x$$

$$x = y^2 - 2y$$

$$\Rightarrow x + 1 = y^2 - 2y + 1$$

$$\Rightarrow x + 1 = (y-1)^2$$

$$\Rightarrow y = 1 \pm \sqrt{x + 1}$$

$$\int_0^4 \left[\int_{y^2-2y}^{2y} f(x,y)dx \right] dy$$

$$= \int_{-1}^0 \left[\int_{1-\sqrt{x+1}}^{1+\sqrt{x+1}} f(x,y)dy \right] dx + \int_0^8 \left[\int_{\frac{1}{2}x}^{1+\sqrt{x+1}} f(x,y)dy \right] dx$$

31.

$$\int_0^1 \left[\int_{1-x}^{2-x} (x+y)dy \right] dx$$

$$= \int_0^1 \left[\int_{1-y}^{1} (x+y)dx \right] dy + \int_1^2 \left[\int_0^{2-y} (x+y)dx \right] dy$$

$$= \int_0^1 \left[\tfrac{1}{2}x^2 + xy \Big|_{1-y}^{1} \right] dy + \int_1^2 \left[\tfrac{1}{2}x^2 + xy \Big|_0^{2-y} \right] dy$$

$$= \int_0^1 \left[\tfrac{1}{2} + y - \tfrac{1}{2}(1-y)^2 - (1-y)y \right] dy$$

$$+ \int_1^2 \left[\tfrac{1}{2}(2-y)^2 + (2-y)y \right] dy$$

$$= \int_0^1 \left[y + \frac{1}{2}y^2 \right] dy + \int_1^2 \left[2 - \frac{1}{2}y^2 \right] dy$$

$$= \left[\frac{1}{2}y^2 + \frac{1}{6}y^3 \right]\Big|_0^1 + \left[2y - \frac{1}{6}y^3 \right]\Big|_1^2 = \frac{3}{2}$$

$y = \sqrt{1+x^2}$

R

1

35. $\int_0^1 \left[\int_0^{\sqrt{1+x^2}} \frac{dy}{x^2+y^2+1} \right] dx$

$$= \int_0^1 \left[\frac{1}{\sqrt{x^2+1}} \tan^{-1}\left(\frac{y}{\sqrt{x^2+1}} \right) \right]\Big|^{\sqrt{1+x^2}} dx$$

$$= \int_0^1 \frac{1}{\sqrt{x^2+1}} (\tan^{-1}1 - \tan^{-1}0)dx = \frac{\pi}{4} \int_0^1 \frac{dx}{\sqrt{x^2+1}}$$

Using the trigonometric substitution $x = \tan u$, the integral becomes

$$\frac{\pi}{4} \int_0^{\pi/4} \frac{\sec^2u \, du}{\sqrt{\tan^2u + 1}} = \frac{\pi}{4} \int_0^{\pi/4} \sec u \, du = \frac{\pi}{4} \ln|\sec u + \tan u| \Big|_0^{\pi/4}$$

$$= \frac{\pi}{4} \ln(\sqrt{2} + 1)$$

Exercise 3, pp. 966-967

3. The curves intersect at $(\pm 3, 0)$.

$$\iint_R dA = \int_{-3}^3 \left[\int_{x^2-9}^{9-x^2} dy \right] dx = \int_{-3}^3 (18-2x^2)dx$$

$$= \int_{-3}^3 (18x-2x^2)dx = (18x - \frac{2x^3}{3})\Big|_{-3}^3$$

$$= (54-18) - (-54+18) = 72$$

7. $\iint dA = \int_2^5 \left[\int_0^{\frac{1}{\sqrt{x-1}}} dy \right] dx = \int_2^5 (x-1)^{-1/2}dx$

$$= 2(x-1)^{1/2}\Big|_2^5 = 2(\sqrt{4} - \sqrt{1}) = 2$$

11. $V = \iint\limits_{R} z \, dA = \iint\limits_{R} (2-x-2y) \, dA$

$$= \int_0^1 \int_0^{2-2y} (2-x-2y) \, dx \, dy = \int_0^1 [(2x - \frac{x^2}{2} - 2xy)\Big|_0^{2-2y}] \, dy$$

$$= \int_0^1 [4 - 4y - \frac{1}{2}(4+4y^2-8y) + 4y(y-1)] \, dy$$

$$= \int_0^1 (2y^2-4y+2) \, dy = (\frac{2}{3} y^3 - 2y^2 + 2y)\Big|_0^1 = \frac{2}{3}$$

15. $V = \iint\limits_{R} z \, dA = \iint\limits_{R} (4-x^2-y^2) \, dA$

$$= \int_0^2 \int_{-\sqrt{4-x^2}}^{\sqrt{4-x^2}} (4-x^2-y^2) \, dy \, dx = 2\int_0^2 \int_0^{\sqrt{4-x^2}} (4-x^2-y^2) \, dy \, dx$$

$$= 2 \int_0^2 [4\sqrt{4-x^2} - x^2\sqrt{4-x^2} - \frac{1}{3}(4-x^2)^{3/2}] \, dx$$

$$= \frac{4}{3} \int_0^2 (4-x^2)^{3/2} \, dx$$

Using $x = 2 \sin u$, we have:

$$\int (4-x^2)^{3/2} \, dx = 16 \int \cos^4 u \, du$$

$$= 16 \int \cos^2 u \, du - 16 \int \cos^2 u \sin^2 u \, du$$

$$= 8 \int (1 + \cos 2u) \, du - 4 \int \sin^2 2u \, du$$

$$= 8u + 4 \sin 2u - 2 \int (1 - \cos 4u) \, du$$

$$= 8u + 4 \sin 2u - 2u + \frac{1}{2} \sin 4u + C$$

Since $x = 0 \Rightarrow u = 0$ and $x = 2 \Rightarrow u = \frac{\pi}{2}$,

$$\text{Volume} = \frac{4}{3} \int_0^2 (4-x^2)^{3/2} \, dx$$

$$= (8u + \frac{16}{3} \sin 2u + \frac{2}{3} \sin 4u)\Big|_0^{\pi/2} = 4\pi$$

19.

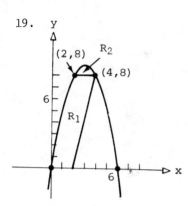

Solving $x^2 - 6x + y = 0$ for x, we obtain

$$x = \frac{6 - \sqrt{36 - 4y}}{2} = 3 - \sqrt{9 - y}$$

left of the parabola's vertex, and $x = 3 + \sqrt{9 - y}$ right of the parabola's vertex. Hence,

$$A = \int_{R_1} dA + \int_{R_2} dA = \int_0^8 \left[\int_{3-\sqrt{9-y}}^{\frac{y+8}{4}} dx \right] dy + \int_8^9 \left[\int_{3-\sqrt{9-y}}^{3+\sqrt{9-y}} dx \right] dy$$

$$= \int_0^8 (\frac{y}{4} + 2 - 3 + \sqrt{9-y})\,dy + \int_8^9 2\sqrt{9 - y}\,dy$$

$$= \frac{y^2}{8} - y - \frac{2}{3}(9-y)^{3/2} \Big|_0^8 - \frac{4}{3}(9-y)^{3/2} \Big|_8^9$$

$$= 8 - 8 - \frac{2}{3}(1^{3/2}) + \frac{2}{3}(9)^{3/2} + \frac{4}{3}(1^{3/2}) = \frac{2}{3} + 18 = \frac{56}{3}$$

23. The solid is the region inside the cylinder $z^2 = 1 - x^2$, and above the triangular region $0 \le x \le 1$, $0 \le y \le x$, formed in the xy plane (i.e. z=0).

27. $\iint_R xy\, dA = \int_0^{\sqrt{2}} \int_{x^2}^{4-x^2} xy\, dy\, dx = \int_0^{\sqrt{2}} [x(\frac{1}{2} y^2)\Big|_{x^2}^{4-x^2}]\,dx$

$$= \frac{1}{2} \int_0^{\sqrt{2}} x(16-8x^2)\,dx = \frac{1}{2} \int_0^{\sqrt{2}} (16x-8x^3)\,dx$$

$$= \frac{1}{2}(8x^2-2x^4)\Big|_0^{\sqrt{2}} = \frac{1}{2}(16-8) = 4$$

31. The solid lies below
the surface $z = xe^y$
and above the region
R in the xy plane.

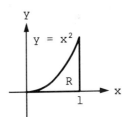

$$V = \int_0^1 \left[\int_0^{x^2} xe^y dy \right] dx$$

$$= \int_0^1 \left[xe^y \Big|_0^{x^2} \right] dx = \int_0^1 \left[xe^{x^2} - x \right] dx$$

$$= \left(\frac{1}{2}e^{x^2} - \frac{1}{2}x^2 \right) \Big|_0^1 = \frac{1}{2}e^1 - \frac{1}{2}e^0 - \frac{1}{2} - 0$$

$$= \frac{1}{2}(e-2)$$

Exercise 4, pp. 973-974

3. The base region here is the right half of a circle
of radius 2, centered at (0,2). This is given by
$r = 4 \sin \theta$, $0 \le \theta \le \dfrac{\pi}{2}$. Hence, the integral
becomes

$$\int_0^{\pi/2} \int_0^{4 \sin \theta} r^2 (r\, dr) d\theta = \int_0^{\pi/2} \left[\frac{r^4}{4} \Big|_0^{4 \sin \theta} \right] d\theta$$

$$= 64 \int_0^{\pi/2} \sin^4 \theta\, d\theta.$$

Now $\int \sin^4 \theta\, d\theta = \int \sin^2 \theta\, d\theta - \int \sin^2 \theta \cos^2 \theta\, d\theta$

$$= \frac{1}{2} \theta - \frac{1}{4} \sin 2\theta - \frac{1}{4} \int \sin^2 2\theta\, d\theta$$

$$= \frac{1}{2} \theta - \frac{1}{4} \sin 2\theta - \frac{1}{8} \theta + \frac{1}{32} \sin 4\theta + C$$

Thus, $64 \int_0^{\pi/2} \sin^4\theta d\theta = 32\theta - 16 \sin 2\theta - 8\theta$

$+ 2 \sin 4\theta |_0^{\pi/2} = 12\pi$

7. R satisfies $1 \le r \le 2$, $0 \le \theta \le \frac{\pi}{2}$.

The integral becomes $\int_0^{\pi/2} \int_1^2 e^{-r^2} r \, dr \, d\theta$

$= \int_0^{\pi/2} \left[-\frac{1}{2} e^{-r^2} \big|_1^2 \right] d\theta = -\frac{1}{2}(e^{-4}-e^{-1})\theta \big|_0^{\pi/2} (e^{-1}-e^{-4})$.

11. The integral becomes $\int_0^{2\pi} \int_0^{3+\cos\theta} r(r \, dr \, d\theta)$

$= \int_0^{2\pi} \frac{1}{3}(3 + \cos\theta)^3 d\theta$

$= \frac{1}{3} \int_0^{2\pi} (27 + 27 \cos\theta + 9 \cos^2\theta + \cos^3\theta) d\theta$

Using $\cos^3\theta = \cos\theta(1 - \sin^2\theta)$ and $\cos^2\theta$

$= (1 + \cos 2\theta)/2$, the original integral yields

$(\frac{1}{3})[27\theta + 27 \sin\theta + (9/2)\theta + (9/4) \sin 2\theta + \sin\theta$

$- (\frac{1}{3})\sin^3\theta]\big|_0^{2\pi}$ or 21π

15. $\int_{\frac{\pi}{2}}^{\pi} \left[\int_0^1 r \cos\theta \, dr \right] d\theta$

$= \int_{\frac{\pi}{2}}^{\pi} \left[\frac{1}{2}r^2 \cos\theta \big|_0^1 \right] d\theta$

$= \int_{\frac{\pi}{2}}^{\pi} \frac{1}{2} \cos\theta \, d\theta = \frac{1}{2} \sin\theta \big|_{\frac{\pi}{2}}^{\pi} = 0 - \frac{1}{2} = -\frac{1}{2}$

19. Letting $x = r \cos \theta$ and $y = r \sin \theta$, we find that the circle $x^2 + y^2 = ay$ has polar equation $r^2 = ar \sin \theta$, or $r = a \sin \theta$. Our limits on r and θ are thus $0 \leq \theta \leq \pi$ and $0 \leq r \leq a \sin \theta$. At any point (r, θ) in the interior of our circle, the intercepts of the sphere are $z = \pm \sqrt{a^2 - x^2 - y^2}$ $= \pm\sqrt{a^2 - r^2}$. The volume sought is thus

$$2 \int_0^\pi \left[\int_0^{a \sin \theta} f(r, \theta) r \, dr \right] d\theta = 2 \int_0^\pi \int_0^{a \sin \theta} r\sqrt{a^2 - r^2} \, dr \, d\theta$$

$$= 2 \int_0^\pi \left[-\frac{1}{3} (a^2 - r^2)^{3/2} \Big|_0^{a \sin \theta} \right] d\theta$$

$$= \frac{2}{3} \int_0^\pi [a^3 - a^3(1 - \sin^2 \theta)^{3/2}] d\theta$$

$$= \frac{2}{3} a^2 [\pi - \int_0^\pi |\cos^3 \theta| d\theta] = \frac{2}{3} a^3 [\pi - 2 \int_0^{\pi/2} \cos^3 \theta \, d\theta]$$

$$= \frac{2}{3} a^3 \left[\pi - 2(\sin \theta - \frac{1}{3} \sin^3 \theta) \Big|_0^{\pi/2} \right] = \frac{2}{3} a^3 (\pi - \frac{4}{3})$$

$$= \frac{2a^3}{9} (3\pi - 4)$$

23. The leaf in the first quadrant satisfies $0 \leq \theta \leq \frac{\pi}{3}$, and $0 \leq r \leq \sin 3\theta$. The area is thus

$$\int_0^{\pi/3} \int_0^{\sin 3\theta} r \, dr \, d\theta = \int_0^{\pi/3} [(\frac{1}{2} r^2) \Big|_0^{\sin 3\theta}] d\theta$$

$$= \frac{1}{2} \int_0^{\pi/3} \sin^2(3\theta) d\theta$$

$$= \frac{1}{2} \int_0^{\pi/3} (\frac{1 - \cos 6\theta}{2}) d\theta$$

$$= \frac{1}{4} (\theta - \frac{1}{6} \sin 6\theta) \Big|_0^{\pi/3} = \frac{\pi}{12}.$$

27. The cardioid intersects the circle for $\cos \theta = -\frac{1}{2}$, or $\theta = \pm \frac{2\pi}{3}$. The region described is given by $-\frac{2\pi}{3} \leq \theta \leq \frac{2\pi}{3}$, $\frac{1}{2} \leq r \leq 1 + \cos \theta$. The area sought is thus $\int_{-2\pi/3}^{2\pi/3} \int_{1/2}^{1+\cos \theta} r \, dr \, d\theta$

$= 2 \int_{0}^{2\pi/3} \int_{1/2}^{1+\cos \theta} r \, dr \, d\theta = 2 \int_{0}^{2\pi/3} \frac{1}{2} r^2 \Big|_{\frac{1}{2}}^{1 + \cos \theta} d\theta$

$= \int_{0}^{2\pi/3} (\frac{3}{4} + 2 \cos \theta + \cos^2 \theta) d\theta$

$= (\frac{3}{4}\theta + 2 \sin \theta + \frac{1}{2}\theta + \frac{1}{4} \sin 2\theta) \Big|_{0}^{2\pi/3}$

$= \frac{5\pi}{6} + 2 \sin (\frac{2\pi}{3}) + \frac{1}{4}\sin (\frac{4\pi}{3}) = \frac{5\pi}{6} + \frac{7\sqrt{3}}{8}$

31. $0 \leq r \leq \frac{\sqrt{2}}{2}$ and $\sin^{-1} r \leq \theta \leq \cos^{-1} r$ produce the region R. When we reverse the order of integration, we must consider two regions $0 \leq r \leq \sin \theta$ for $0 \leq \theta \leq \frac{\pi}{4}$ and $0 \leq r \leq \cos \theta$ for $\frac{\pi}{4} \leq \theta \leq \frac{\pi}{2}$.

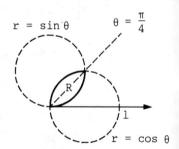

$\int_{0}^{\sqrt{2}/2} \left[\int_{\sin^{-1} r}^{\cos^{-1} r} f(r, \theta) \, d\theta \right] dr$

$\int_{0}^{\pi/4} \left[\int_{0}^{\sin \theta} f(r, \theta) \, dr \right] d\theta + \int_{\pi/4}^{\pi/2} \left[\int_{0}^{\cos \theta} f(r, \theta) \, dr \right] d\theta$

3. $m = \iint\limits_{R} \rho(x,y)\,dA = \int\limits_{0}^{1} \int\limits_{y^2}^{1} (2x+3y)\,dx\,dy$

$\qquad = \int\limits_{0}^{1} [(x^2+3xy)\big|_{y^2}^{1}]\,dy = \int\limits_{0}^{1} (1+3y-y^4-3y^3)\,dy$

$\qquad = (y + \frac{3}{2} y^2 - \frac{1}{5} y^5 - \frac{3}{4} y^4)\big|_{0}^{1} = 1 + \frac{3}{2} - \frac{1}{5} - \frac{3}{4} = \frac{31}{20}$

$M_y = \iint\limits_{R} x\rho(x,y)\,dA = \int\limits_{0}^{1} \int\limits_{y^2}^{1} (2x^2+3xy)\,dx\,dy$

$\qquad = \int\limits_{0}^{1} [(\frac{2}{3} x^3 + \frac{3}{2} x^2 y)\big|_{y^2}^{1}]\,dy$

$\qquad = \int\limits_{0}^{1} (\frac{2}{3} + \frac{3}{2} y - \frac{2}{3} y^6 - \frac{3}{2} y^5)\,dy$

$\qquad = (\frac{2}{3} y + \frac{3}{4} y^2 - \frac{2}{21} y^7 - \frac{1}{4} y^6)\big|_{0}^{1}$

$\qquad = \frac{2}{3} + \frac{3}{4} - \frac{2}{21} - \frac{1}{4} = \frac{15}{14}$

$M_x = \iint\limits_{R} y\rho(x,y)\,dA = \int\limits_{0}^{1} \int\limits_{y^2}^{1} (2xy+3y^2)\,dx\,dy$

$\qquad = \int\limits_{0}^{1} [(x^2 y + 3xy^2)\big|_{y^2}^{1}]\,dy = \int\limits_{0}^{1} (y + 3y^2 - y^5 - 3y^4)\,dy$

$\qquad = (\frac{y^2}{2} + y^3 - \frac{y^6}{6} - \frac{3}{5} y^5)\big|_{0}^{1} = \frac{1}{2} + 1 - \frac{1}{6} - \frac{3}{5} = \frac{11}{15}$

$(\bar{x},\bar{y}) = \frac{1}{m}(M_y, M_x) = (\frac{150}{217}, \frac{44}{93})$

7. $m = \iint\limits_{R} \rho(x,y)\,dA = k\int\limits_{0}^{2}\int\limits_{0}^{3-\frac{3}{2}y} (x+y)\,dx\,dy$

$\qquad = k\int\limits_{0}^{2} [(\frac{x^2}{2} + xy)\big|_{0}^{3-\frac{3}{2}y}]\,dy$

$$= k\int_0^2 \left[\frac{1}{2}(3 - \frac{3}{2}y)^2 + 3y - \frac{3}{2}y^2\right]dy$$

$$= k\int_0^2 \left(\frac{9}{2} - \frac{9}{2}y + \frac{9}{8}y^2 + 3y - \frac{3}{2}y^2\right)dy$$

$$= k\int_0^2 \left(\frac{9}{2} - \frac{3}{2}y - \frac{3}{8}y^2\right)dy = \left(\frac{9}{2}y - \frac{3}{4}y^2 - \frac{1}{8}y^3\right)\Big|_0^2$$

$$= k(9 - 3 - 1) = 5k$$

$$M_y = k\iint_R x\rho(x,y)dA = k\int_0^2 \int_0^{3 - \frac{3}{2}y} (x^2 + xy)dx\, dy$$

$$= k\int_0^2 \left[\left(\frac{x^3}{3} + \frac{x^2y}{2}\right)\Big|_0^{3 - \frac{3}{2}y}\right]dy$$

$$= k\int_0^2 \left(3 - \frac{3}{2}y\right)^2 \left[\frac{1}{3}\left(3 - \frac{3}{2}y\right) + \frac{1}{2}y\right]dy$$

$$= k\int_0^2 \left(9 - 9y + \frac{9}{4}y^2\right)dy = k\left(9y - \frac{9}{2}y^2 + \frac{3}{4}y^3\right)\Big|_0^2$$

$$= k(18 - 18 + 6) = 6k$$

$$M_x = k\iint_R y\rho(x,y)dA = k\int_0^2 \left(\frac{9}{2}y - \frac{3}{2}y^2 - \frac{3}{8}y^3\right)dy$$

(using the integral for m above)

$$= k\left(\frac{9}{4}y^2 - \frac{1}{2}y^3 - \frac{3}{32}y^4\right)\Big|_0^2 = k\left(9 - 4 - \frac{3}{2}\right) = \frac{7k}{2}$$

$$(\overline{x},\overline{y}) = \frac{1}{m}(M_y, M_x) = \left(\frac{6}{5}, \frac{7}{10}\right)$$

11. $$m = \iint_R \rho(r,\theta)dA = k\int_{\pi/6}^{5\pi/6} \int_a^{2a \sin\theta} \frac{1}{r}\, r\, dr\, d\theta$$

$$= ak\int_{\pi/6}^{5\pi/6} (2\sin\theta - 1)d\theta = ak\, (-2\cos\theta - \theta)\Big|_{\pi/6}^{5\pi/6}$$

$$= ak[2 \cos\left(\frac{\pi}{6}\right) - 2 \cos\left(\frac{5\pi}{6}\right) - \frac{2\pi}{3}] = ak(2\sqrt{3} - \frac{2}{3}\pi)$$

By symmetry, $M_y = \bar{x} = 0$.

$$M_x = \iint_R r \sin\theta \, \rho(r,\theta) dA = k \int_{\pi/6}^{5\pi/6} \int_a^{2a \sin\theta} r \sin\theta \, dr \, d\theta$$

$$= k \int_{\pi/6}^{5\pi/6} \frac{1}{2}(4a^2 \sin^3\theta - a^2 \sin\theta) d\theta$$

$$= \frac{ka^2}{2} \int_{\pi/6}^{5\pi/6} (4 \sin^3\theta - \sin\theta) d\theta \ [\text{use } \sin^3\theta = \sin\theta(1 - \cos^2\theta)]$$

$$= \frac{ka^2}{2}\left(\frac{4}{3} \cos^3\theta - 4 \cos\theta + \cos\theta\right)\Big|_{\pi/6}^{5\pi/6}$$

$$= ka^2\left(\frac{3\sqrt{3}}{2} - \frac{4}{3}\left(\frac{\sqrt{3}}{2}\right)^3\right) = ka^2\sqrt{3}$$

$$(\bar{x},\bar{y}) = \frac{1}{m}(M_y,M_x) = (0, \ a\sqrt{3}/(2\sqrt{3} - \frac{2}{3}\pi))$$

5. $$I_x = \iint_R y^2\rho(x,y) dA = \int_0^b \int_0^a \rho \, y^2 dx \, dy$$

$$= \rho \int_0^b ay^2 dy = a\rho \frac{y^3}{3}\Big|_0^b = \rho ab^3/3$$

9. $$I_x = \iint_R y^2 \rho(x,y) dA$$

$$= \rho \int_{-b}^b \int_{-a\sqrt{1-y^2/b^2}}^{a\sqrt{1-y^2/b^2}} y^2 dx \, dy = 2a\rho \int_{-b}^b y^2\sqrt{1 - y^2/b^2} \, dy$$

$$= 4 \frac{a}{b} \rho \int_0^b y^2\sqrt{b^2 - y^2} \, dy$$

Setting $y = b \sin \theta$, this becomes

$$4ab^3\rho \int_0^{\pi/2} \sin^2\theta \cos^2\theta \, d\theta = ab^3\rho \int_0^{\pi/2} \sin^2(2\theta) \, d\theta = \frac{ab^3\rho\pi}{4}$$

23. $m = \iint\limits_R \rho(r,\theta) \, dA = k \int_{-\pi/4}^{\pi/4} \int_{a \sec \theta}^{2a \cos \theta} \left(\frac{1}{r \cos \theta}\right) r \, dr \, d\theta$

$= 2k \int_0^{\pi/4} \sec \theta (2a \cos \theta - a \sec \theta) \, d\theta$

$= 2k \int_0^{\pi/4} (2a - a \sec^2\theta) \, d\theta = (4ka)\frac{\pi}{4} - (2ka) \tan \frac{\pi}{4}$

$= ak(\pi - 2)$

By symmetry, $\overline{y} = M_x = 0$.

Finally, $M_y = \iint\limits_R \rho(r,\theta)(r \cos \theta) \, dA$

$M_y = 2k \int_0^{\pi/4} \int_{a \sec \theta}^{2a \cos \theta} r \, dr \, d\theta = k \int_0^{\pi/4} [4a^2\cos^2\theta - a^2\sec^2\theta] \, d\theta$

$= a^2 k \int_0^{\pi/4} [2 + 2 \cos 2\theta - \sec^2\theta] \, d\theta = a^2 k [2\theta + \sin 2\theta - \tan\theta] \Big|_0^{\pi/4}$

Hence, $M_y = \frac{\pi}{2} ka^2$, and $(\overline{x}, \overline{y}) = \frac{1}{m}(M_y, M_x)$

$= \left(\frac{\pi a}{2(\pi-2)}, 0\right)$.

27. $m = \iint\limits_R \rho(r,\theta) \, dA = k \int_{-\pi/6}^{\pi/6} \int_{2\sqrt{3}}^{4 \cos \theta} \left(\frac{1}{r}\right) r \, dr \, d\theta$

$= 2k \int_0^{\pi/6} (4 \cos \theta - 2\sqrt{3}) \, d\theta = 8k \sin \frac{\pi}{6} - 4\sqrt{3}k \frac{\pi}{6}$

$= 4k\left(1 - \frac{\sqrt{3}\pi}{6}\right)$

By symmetry, $M_x = \overline{y} = 0$.

Finally, $M_y = \iint\limits_R \rho(r,\theta) r \cos\theta \, dA$

$$= k \int\limits_{-\pi/6}^{\pi/6} \int\limits_{2\sqrt{3}}^{4\cos\theta} r \cos\theta \, dr \, d\theta$$

$$= k \int\limits_{0}^{\pi/6} (16 \cos^3\theta - 12 \cos\theta) d\theta$$

$$= 4k \int\limits_{0}^{\pi/6} [4(1-\sin^2\theta)\cos\theta - 3 \cos\theta \, d\theta]$$

$$= 4k \sin\frac{\pi}{6} - \frac{16}{3} k \sin^3(\frac{\pi}{6}) = \frac{4}{3} k$$

Hence, $(\bar{x},\bar{y}) = \frac{1}{m}(M_y, M_x) = (\frac{2}{6 - \sqrt{3}\,\pi} , 0) \approx (3.58, 0)$

31. $m = \int_R \int \rho(x,y) dA = \int\limits_{-2}^{1} \left[\int\limits_{y-2}^{-y^2} x^2 dx \right] dy$

$$= \int\limits_{-2}^{1} \left[\frac{1}{3}x^3 \Big|_{y-2}^{-y^2} \right] dx = \frac{1}{3} \int\limits_{-2}^{1} [-y^6 - (y-2)^3] dy$$

$$= -\frac{1}{3}(\frac{1}{7}y^7 + \frac{1}{4}(y-2)^4)\Big|_{-2}^{1} = -\frac{1}{3}[\frac{1}{7} + \frac{1}{4} + \frac{128}{7} - \frac{256}{4}]$$

$$= -\frac{1}{3}[-\frac{1269}{28}] = \frac{423}{28}$$

$M_x = \int_R \int y\rho(x,y) dA = \int\limits_{-2}^{1} \left[\int\limits_{y-2}^{-y^2} yx^2 dx \right] dy$

$M_x = \int\limits_{-2}^{1} \left[y(\frac{1}{3}x^3) \Big|_{y-2}^{-y^2} \right] dx$

$$= \frac{1}{3} \int\limits_{-2}^{1} [-y^7 - y(y-2)^3] dy$$

$$= -\frac{1}{3} \int\limits_{-2}^{1} [y^7 + (y-2)^4 + 2(y-2)^3] dy$$

$$= -\frac{1}{3}[\frac{1}{8}y^8 + \frac{1}{5}(y-2)^5 + \frac{1}{2}(y-2)^4]\Big|_{-2}^{1}$$

$$= -\frac{1}{3}[\frac{1}{8} - \frac{1}{5} + \frac{1}{2} - \frac{256}{8} + \frac{1024}{5} - \frac{256}{2}] = -\frac{603}{40}$$

$$M_y = \int_R \int xp(x,\, y)dA = \int_{-2}^{1}\left[\int_{y-2}^{y^2} x \cdot x^2\ dx\right]dy$$

$$= \int_{-2}^{1}\left[\frac{1}{4}x^4\ \Big|_{y-2}^{-y^2}\right]dy = \frac{1}{4}\int_{-2}^{1}[y^8 - (y-2)^4]dy$$

$$= \frac{1}{4}[\frac{1}{9}y^9 - \frac{1}{5}(y-2)^5]\ \Big|_{-2}^{1} = \frac{1}{4}[\frac{1}{9} + \frac{1}{5} + \frac{512}{9} - \frac{1024}{5}]$$

$$= \frac{1}{4}[\frac{-6642}{45}] = \frac{-369}{10}$$

Center of mass $= (\bar{x},\ \bar{y}) = \left(\dfrac{M_y}{m},\ \dfrac{M_x}{m}\right) = \left(\dfrac{-3444}{1410},\ \dfrac{-1407}{1410}\right)$

Exercise 6, pp. 988-989

3. $z = f(x,y) = 4 - x^2 - y^2;\quad f_x(x,y) = -2x;$

$f_y(x,y) = -2y$

Hence, $S = \int_R\int \sqrt{f_x^{\,2} + f_y^{\,2} + 1}\ dA = \int_R\int \sqrt{4x^2 + 4y^2 + 1}\ dA$

Because of the integrand and the circular base region, we convert to polar coordinates:

$$S = \int_0^{2\pi}\int_0^2 \sqrt{1 + 4r^2}\ r\ dr\ d\theta = \int_0^{2\pi}(\frac{1}{12}(1+4r^2)^{3/2}\ \Big|_0^2)d\theta$$

$$= \frac{1}{12}(17^{3/2} - 1)\theta\ \Big|_0^{2\pi} = \frac{\pi}{6}(17\sqrt{17} - 1)$$

7. $z = f(x,y) = xy;\quad f_x(x,y) = y;\quad f_y(x,y) = x$

$S = \int_R\int \sqrt{f_x^{\,2} + f_y^{\,2} + 1}\ dA = \int_R\int \sqrt{y^2 + x^2 + 1}\ dA$

Now R is the quarter-disk of radius a, centered at the origin, and lying in the first quadrant. Polar coordinates are more convenient for both R and the integrand:

$$S = \int_0^{\pi/2} \int_0^a \sqrt{r^2 + 1} \; r \; dr \; d\theta = \int_0^{\pi/2} [\frac{1}{3}(r^2+1)^{3/2} \Big|_0^a] d\theta$$

$$= \frac{\pi}{6}[(a^2+1)^{3/2} - 1]$$

11. The upper half is the surface above the base region $0 \le r \le a$, with equation $z = f(x,y) = \sqrt{a^2 - x^2 - y^2}$.

   This gives $f_x(x,y) = \dfrac{-x}{\sqrt{a^2 - x^2 - y^2}}$ and $f_y(x,y)$

   $= \dfrac{-y}{\sqrt{a^2 - x^2 - y^2}}$. The upper hemisphere then has area

   $\iint\limits_R \sqrt{f_x^{\;2} + f_y^{\;2} + 1} \; dA = a \iint\limits_R \dfrac{dA}{\sqrt{a^2 - x^2 - y^2}}$. In polar

   coordinates, this is $a\int_0^{2\pi} \int_0^a \dfrac{r \; dr \; d\theta}{\sqrt{a^2 - r^2}} = 2\pi a(-\sqrt{a^2 - r^2}) \Big|_0^a$

   $= 2\pi a^2$. Total surface area is therefore $4\pi a^2$.

15. To find the surface area of $z = 9 - x^2 - y^2$ between the planes $z = 0$ (the xy plane) and $z = 8$, we will compute two surface areas and subtract:

   S_T: below $z = 9 - x^2 - y^2$, above the region $x^2 + y^2 = 9$ in the xy plane

   S_S: below $z = 9 - x^2 - y^2$, above the region $x^2 + y^2 = 1$ in the xy plane

   Note: Both of these surface areas are most easily down in polar coordinates.

   $f(x,y) = 9 - x^2 - y^2 \Rightarrow f_x = -2x, \; f_y = -2y$

   $\Rightarrow \sqrt{f_x^2 + f_y^2 + 1} = \sqrt{4x^2 + 4y^2 + 1} = \sqrt{4r^2 + 1}$

   $S_T = \int_0^{2\pi} \left[\int_0^3 \sqrt{4r^2 + 1} \; r \; dr \right] d\theta$

$$= \int_0^{2\pi} \left[\frac{1}{12}(4r^2+1)^{3/2} \Big|_0^3 \right] d\theta = \int_0^\pi \left[\frac{(37)^{3/2} - 1}{12} \right] d\theta$$

$$= \frac{1}{12} \left[(37)^{3/2} - 1 \right] \theta \Big|_0^{2\pi} = \frac{\pi}{6} 37\sqrt{37} - \frac{\pi}{6}$$

$$S_S = \int_0^{2\pi} \left[\int_0^1 \sqrt{4r^2 + 1} \; r \; dr \right] d\theta$$

$$= \int_0^{2\pi} \left[\frac{1}{12}(4r^2+1)^{3/2} \Big|_0^1 \right] d\theta = \int_0^{2\pi} \left[\frac{(5)^{3/2} - 1}{12} \right] d\theta$$

$$= \frac{1}{12} \left[(5)^{3/2} - 1 \right] \theta \Big|_0^{2\pi} = \frac{\pi}{6} 5\sqrt{5} - \frac{\pi}{6}$$

The surface area that we want is

$$S = S_T - S_S = \frac{\pi}{6}(37\sqrt{37} - 5\sqrt{5})$$

Exercise 7, pp. 995-996

3. $\displaystyle \int_0^3 \left\{ \int_z^{z+2} \left[\int_y^{y+z} 2x \; dx \right] dy \right\} dz$

$$= \int_0^3 \left\{ \int_z^{z+2} (2yz + z^2) dy \right\} dz = \int_0^3 \left\{ (y^2z + z^2y) \Big|_z^{z+2} \right\} dz$$

$$= \int_0^3 (4z^2 + 4z + 2z^2) dz = \int_0^3 (6z^2 + 4z) dz = 2z^3 + 2z^2 \Big|_0^3$$

$$= 54 + 18 = 72$$

7. (1) $\displaystyle \int_0^6 \left\{ \int_0^{3-\frac{x}{2}} \left[\int_0^{2-\frac{x}{3}-\frac{2}{3}y} f(x,y,z)dz \right] dy \right\} dx$

(2) $\displaystyle \int_0^3 \left\{ \int_0^{6-2y} \left[\int_0^{2-\frac{x}{3}-\frac{2}{3}y} f(x,y,z)dz \right] dx \right\} dy$

(3) $\displaystyle \int_0^6 \left\{ \int_0^{2-\frac{1}{3}x} \left[\int_0^{3-\frac{x}{2}-\frac{3}{2}z} f(x,y,z)dy \right] dz \right\} dx$

(4) $\int_0^2 \left\{ \int_0^{6-3z} \left[\int_0^{3 - \frac{x}{2} - \frac{3}{2}z} f(x,y,z)\,dy \right] dx \right\} dz$

(5) $\int_0^3 \left\{ \int_0^{2 - \frac{2}{3}y} \left[\int_0^{6-3z-2y} f(x,y,z)\,dx \right] dz \right\} dy$

(6) $\int_0^2 \left\{ \int_0^{3 - \frac{3}{2}z} \left[\int_0^{6-3z-2y} f(x,y,z)\,dx \right] dy \right\} dz$

11. Our base region R is the semi-disk $x^2 + y^2 \le 9$, $y \ge 0$. Since $0 \le z \le 3 - x$, we have

$\iiint\limits_S (xy+3y)\,dV$

$= \int_{-3}^3 \left\{ \int_0^{\sqrt{9-x^2}} [\int_0^{3-x}(x+3)y\,dz]\,dy \right\} dx$

$= \int_{-3}^3 \left\{ \int_0^{\sqrt{9-x^2}} (x+3)(3-x)y\,dy \right\} dx$

$= \int_{-3}^3 \left\{ (9-x^2)\frac{1}{2}y^2 \Big|_0^{\sqrt{9-x^2}} \right\} dx$

$= \int_{-3}^3 \frac{1}{2}(9-x^2)^2\,dx = \frac{1}{2}\int_{-3}^3 (81-18x^2+x^4)\,dx = \frac{1}{2}(81x-6x^3+\frac{1}{5}x^5)\Big|_{-3}^3 = \frac{648}{5}$

15. We let the base region R be the region in the yz-plane bounded by $z = y$ and $z = y^2$. Over this region we have $0 \le x \le y - z$. Hence,

$$\text{Volume} = \int_0^1 \int_{y2}^y \int_0^{y-z} dx\ dz\ dy = \int_0^1 \int_{y^2}^y (y-z)dz\ dy$$

$$= \int_0^1 [(yz - \frac{1}{2} z^2)|_{y2}^y]dy$$

$$= \int_0^1 (y^2 - \frac{1}{2} y^2 - y^3 + \frac{1}{2} y^4)dy$$

$$= (\frac{1}{6} y^3 - \frac{1}{4} y^4 + \frac{1}{10} y^5)|_0^1 = \frac{1}{60}$$

19. $m = \iiint\limits_S \rho dV = k \int_0^{2\pi} \int_0^a [\int_0^h r^2 dz]r\ dr\ d\theta = k \int_0^{2\pi} \int_0^a r^3 h\ dr\ d\theta$

$$= \frac{kh}{4} \int_0^{2\pi} (r^4)|_0^a\ d\theta = 2\pi(\frac{kh}{4})a^4 = k\pi a^4 h/2$$

Exercise 8, p. 1002

3. $(x,y,z) = (1,1,\sqrt{2})$

$\theta = \tan^{-1}(\frac{y}{x}) = \tan^{-1}(\frac{1}{1}) = \frac{\pi}{4}$

$r^2 = x^2 + y^2 = 1 + 1 = 2 \Rightarrow$ choose $r = \sqrt{2}$ since

x and y are both positive. Thus, $(r,\theta,z) = (\sqrt{2},\frac{\pi}{4},\sqrt{2})$.

Note: $(-\sqrt{2}, \frac{5\pi}{4}, \sqrt{2})$ also works.

7. $(r,\theta,z) = (4,\frac{\pi}{6},2)$

$x = r \cos \theta = 4 \cos \frac{\pi}{6} = 4(\frac{\sqrt{3}}{2}) = 2\sqrt{3}$

$y = r \sin \theta = 4 \sin \frac{\pi}{6} = 4(\frac{1}{2}) = 2$

Thus, $(x,y,z) = (2\sqrt{3},2,2)$

11. $m = \iiint\limits_M \rho dV = k \int_0^{2\pi} \int_0^a \int_{-\sqrt{a^2-r^2}}^{\sqrt{a^2-r^2}} dz(r\ dr\ d\theta)$

$$= 2k \int_0^{2\pi} \int_0^a r\sqrt{a^2-r^2}\ dr\ d\theta$$

$$= 2k \int_0^{2\pi} [-\frac{1}{3}(a^2-r^2)^{3/2}\big|_0^a] \, d\theta = 4\pi k(\frac{1}{3}a^3) = \frac{4}{3}\pi ka^3$$

15. By symmetry $\bar{x} = \bar{y} = 0$. Now the mass

$$m = \iiint_S \rho dV = k \int_0^{2\pi} \int_0^{\sqrt{3}} \int_{r^2}^{\sqrt{12-r^2}} dz \, r \, dr \, d\theta$$

$$= k\int_0^{2\pi}\int_0^{\sqrt{3}} (r\sqrt{12-r^2} - r^3)dr \, d\theta$$

$$= k\int_0^{2\pi} [-\frac{1}{3}(12-r^2)^{3/2} - \frac{1}{4}r^4]\big|_0^{\sqrt{3}} \, d\theta$$

$$= k\int_0^{2\pi}(8\sqrt{3} - \frac{45}{4})d\theta = k(8\sqrt{3} - \frac{45}{4})\theta\big|_0^{2\pi} = 2\pi k(8\sqrt{3} - \frac{45}{4})$$

Next, $m\bar{z} = k \int_0^{2\pi} \int_0^{\sqrt{3}} \int_{r^2}^{\sqrt{12-r^2}} z \, dz \, r \, dr \, d\theta$

$$= \frac{k}{2}\int_0^{2\pi} \int_0^{\sqrt{3}} r(12-r^2-r^4)dr \, d\theta$$

$$= \frac{k}{2}\int_0^{2\pi} (6r^2 - \frac{1}{4}r^4 - \frac{1}{6}r^6\big|_0^{\sqrt{3}})d\theta = \frac{k}{2}\int_0^{2\pi}(\frac{45}{4})d\theta = \frac{45k}{8}\theta\big|_0^{2\pi} = \frac{45k\pi}{4}$$

Hence, $(\bar{x}, \bar{y}, \bar{z}) = (0, 0, \dfrac{45}{64\sqrt{3}-90}) \cong (0, 0, 2.16)$.

Exercise 9, pp. 1009-1010

3. $(x,y,z) = (1,1,\sqrt{2})$

$$\theta = \tan^{-1}(\frac{y}{x}) = \tan^{-1}(\frac{1}{1}) = \frac{\pi}{4}$$

$$\rho = \sqrt{x^2 + y^2 + z^2} = \sqrt{1 + 1 + 2} = 2$$

$$\emptyset = \cos^{-1}(\frac{z}{\rho}) = \cos^{-1}(\frac{\sqrt{2}}{2}) = \frac{\pi}{4}$$

Thus $(\rho,\theta,\emptyset) = (2,\frac{\pi}{4}.\frac{\pi}{4})$.

7. $(x,y,z) = (0, 3\sqrt{3}, 3)$

$\theta = \tan^{-1}(\frac{y}{x}) \Rightarrow \theta = \frac{\pi}{2}$ since $x = 0$ and $y > 0$

$\rho = \sqrt{x^2 + y^2 + z^2} = \sqrt{0 + 27 + 9} = 6$

$\emptyset = \cos^{-1}(\frac{z}{\rho}) = \cos^{-1}(\frac{3}{6}) = \frac{\pi}{3}$. Thus, $(\rho, \theta, \emptyset) = (6, \frac{\pi}{2}, \frac{\pi}{3})$.

11. $\int_0^{\pi/2} \{ \int_0^{\sin\phi} [\int_0^{\pi/4} \rho^2 \sin\phi \, d\theta] d\rho \} \, d\phi$

$= \frac{\pi}{4} \int_0^{\pi/2} [\int_0^{\sin\phi} \rho^2 \sin\phi \, d\rho] d\phi = \frac{\pi}{12} \int_0^{\pi/2} \sin^4\phi \, d\phi$

$= \frac{\pi}{12} \int_0^{\pi/2} (\frac{1-\cos 2\phi}{2})^2 \, d\phi = \frac{\pi}{48} \int_0^{\pi/2} (1 - 2\cos 2\phi + \cos^2 2\phi) d$

$= \frac{\pi}{48} \int_0^{\pi/2} (\frac{3}{2} - 2\cos 2\phi + \frac{1}{2} \cos 4\phi) d\phi$

$= \frac{\pi}{48} (\frac{3}{2} \phi - \sin 2\phi + \frac{1}{8} \sin 4\phi)|_0^{\pi/2} = \frac{\pi^2}{64}$

15. $m = k \iiint_S \rho^2 \sin\phi \, d\rho \, d\theta \, d\phi = k \int_0^{\pi} \int_0^{2\pi} \int_0^{a} \rho^2 \sin\phi \, d\rho \, d\theta \, d\phi$

$= \frac{k}{3} a^3 \int_0^{\pi} \int_0^{2\pi} \sin\phi \, d\theta \, d\phi = \frac{2\pi k}{3} a^3 \int_0^{\pi} \sin\phi \, d\phi$

$= \frac{2\pi k a^3}{3} (-\cos\pi + \cos 0) = \frac{4}{3} \pi k a^3$

19. The region of integration has base R which is a quarter-disk of radius 2 in the first quadrant. In cylindrical coordinates, the integral becomes

$\int_0^2 [\int_0^{\pi/2} \int_0^2 (r) r \, dr \, d\theta] dz = \int_0^2 \int_0^{\pi/2} \frac{8}{3} d\theta \, dz = (2)(\frac{\pi}{2})(\frac{8}{3}) = \frac{8\pi}{3}$

23. Let S be a sphere of radius a centered at the origin.

Rectangular coordinates:

$x^2 + y^2 + z^2 = a^2$

$$\iiint_S f(x,y,z)dV = \int_{-a}^{a}\left\{\int_{-\sqrt{a^2-x^2}}^{+\sqrt{a^2-x^2}}\left[\int_{-\sqrt{a^2-x^2-y^2}}^{+\sqrt{a^2-x^2-y^2}} f(x,y,z)dz\right]dy\right\}dx$$

Cylindrical coordinates:

$z^2 + r^2 = a^2, \ 0 \leq \theta \leq 2\pi, \ 0 \leq r \leq a$

$$\iiint_S f(x,y,z)dV = \int_{0}^{2\pi}\left\{\int_{0}^{a}\left[\int_{-\sqrt{a^2-r^2}}^{+\sqrt{a^2-r^2}} f(r\cos\theta, y\sin\theta, z)rdz\right]dr\right\}d\theta$$

Spherical coordinates:

$0 \leq \rho \leq a, \ 0 \leq \theta \leq 2\pi, \ 0 \leq \emptyset \leq \pi$

$$\iiint_S f(x,y,z)dV$$
$$= \int_{0}^{2\pi}\left\{\int_{0}^{\pi}\left[\int_{0}^{a} f(\rho\sin\emptyset\cos\theta, \rho\sin\emptyset\sin\theta, \rho\cos\emptyset)\rho^2\sin\emptyset d\rho\right]d\emptyset\right\}d\theta$$

27. From the integral we have:

$0 \leq r \leq \sqrt{9 - z^2}, \ 0 \leq z \leq 3,$ and $0 \leq \theta \leq \pi$

This is a quarter of a sphere of radius 3. It is located above the xy plane in the two octants where y is positive.

Note: $r^2\sin\theta \ dr \ dz \ d\theta = r\sin\theta(r \ dr \ dz \ d\theta)$

$= y(dz \ dy \ dx)$

$= \rho\sin\emptyset \ \sin\theta(\rho^2\sin\emptyset \ d\rho \ d\emptyset \ d\theta)$

$= \rho^3\sin^2\emptyset \ \sin\theta \ d\rho \ d\emptyset \ d\theta$

The integral then becomes:

$$\int_0^\pi \left\{ \int_0^3 \left[\int_0^{\sqrt{9-r^2}} r^2 \sin\theta \; dr \right] dz \right\} d\theta = \int_0^\pi \left\{ \int_0^{\pi/2} \left[\int_0^3 \rho^3 \sin^2\emptyset \; \sin\theta \; d\rho \right] d\emptyset \right\} d\theta$$

Miscellaneous Exercises, pp. 1010-1012

3. $\displaystyle\int_0^{\pi/4} \left[\int_0^{\tan x} \sec x \; dy \right] dx = \int_0^{\pi/4} \sec x \tan x \; dx$

$= \sec x \Big|_0^{\pi/4} = \sqrt{2} - 1$

7. (a) $\displaystyle\sum_{i=1}^4 f(u_i, v_i) dA_i = (-1)(1)dA_1 + (1)(1)dA_2$

$+ (1)(-1)dA_3 + (-1)(-1)dA_4 = 4[-1 + 1 - 1 + 1] = 0$

(b) Largest value $= (0)(0)dA_1 + (2)(2)dA_2 + (0)(0)dA_3$
$+ (-2)(-2)dA_4 = 4[4 + 4] = 32$

Similarly, the smallest value is $(-2)(2)dA_1$
$+ (0)(0)dA_2 + (2)(-2)dA_3 + (0)(0)dA_4 = -32$

The average of these is 0.

(c) $\displaystyle\int_{-2}^2 \int_{-2}^2 xy \; dx \; dy = \int_{-2}^2 \left[\frac{1}{2}x^2 y \Big|_{-2}^2 \right] dy = 0$

11. $\displaystyle\iint_R x \sin(y^3) dA = \int_0^2 \int_0^y x \sin(y^3) dx \; dy$

$= \displaystyle\int_0^2 \left[\frac{1}{2} x^2 \sin(y^3) \Big|_0^y \right] dy = \frac{1}{2} \int_0^2 y^2 \sin(y^3) dy$

$= \displaystyle\frac{-\cos(y^3)}{6} \Big|_0^2 = (1 - \cos 8)/6$

15. The portion of the ellipsoid in the first octant is given by

$$\int_0^c \int_0^{b\sqrt{1-z^2/c^2}} \int_0^{a\sqrt{1-y^2/b^2-z^2/c^2}} dx\ dy\ dz$$

Under the substitutions $x = au$, $y = bv$, $z = cw$, $dx = adu$, $dy = bdv$, $dz = cdw$, the integral becomes

$$\int_0^1 \int_0^{\sqrt{1-w^2}} \int_0^{\sqrt{1-v^2-w^2}} (abc)\,du\ dv\ dw.\quad \text{But this is just}$$

abc times the volume of the portion of the *unit sphere* (centered at the origin) in the first octant. That is, volume of ellipsoid in first octant equals

$abc[\frac{1}{8}(\frac{4}{3}\pi)]$ or $\frac{abc\pi}{6}$. The whole ellipsoid thus has volume

$8(abc)(\frac{1}{6}\pi) = \frac{4}{3}\pi abc$. When $a = b = c$, we have

$\frac{4}{3}\pi a^3$, which is the volume of a cube of radius a.

19. Mass $m = k \int_0^a \int_{\frac{b}{a^2}x^2}^{\frac{b}{a}x} dy\ dx$, (assuming $a > 0$, $b > 0$)

$$m = \frac{bk}{a} \int_0^a (x - \frac{x^2}{a})dx = \frac{bk}{a}[\frac{x^2}{2} - \frac{x^3}{3a}]\Big|_0^a = \frac{1}{6}(bka)$$

$$M_y = k \int_0^a \int_{\frac{b}{a^2}x^2}^{\frac{b}{a}x} x\ dy\ dx = \frac{bk}{a} \int_0^a (x^2 - \frac{x^3}{a})dx$$

$$= \frac{bk}{a}[\frac{x^3}{3} - \frac{x^4}{4a}]\Big|_0^a = \frac{1}{12}(bka^2)$$

$$M_x = k \int_0^a \int_{\frac{b}{a^2}x^2}^{\frac{b}{a}x} y\ dy\ dx = \frac{1}{2}k(\frac{b}{a})^2 \int_0^a (x^2 - \frac{x^4}{a^2})dx$$

$$= \frac{1}{2} k(\frac{b}{a})^2 [\frac{x^3}{3} - \frac{x^5}{5a^2}]\Big|_0^a = \frac{1}{15} k \frac{b^2}{a^2}(a^3) = \frac{1}{15} kb^2 a$$

Hence, $(\bar{x}, \bar{y}) = (\frac{a}{2}, \frac{2b}{5})$. Although we assumed

$a > 0$, $b > 0$ for the original order of integration, we can see by symmetry that the formula just obtained is valid regardless of the sign of a and b.

23. The solid is a wedge-shaped figure appearing roughly as shown in the figure. Its base in the xy-plane is a parabolic section, and its slanted top is planar. The other five integrals representing this volume are

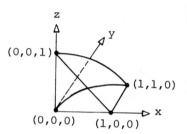

$$\int_0^1 \int_0^{\sqrt{x}} \int_0^{1-x} dz\ dy\ dx = \int_0^1 \int_0^{1-x} \int_0^{\sqrt{x}} dy\ dz\ dx$$

$$= \int_0^1 \int_0^{1-z} \int_0^{\sqrt{x}} dy\ dx\ dz = \int_0^1 \int_0^{\sqrt{1-z}} \int_{y^2}^1 dx\ dy\ dz$$

$$= \int_0^1 \int_0^{1-y^2} \int_{y^2}^1 dx\ dz\ dy$$

27. (a) Since the variable of integration may be changed,

$$I_a = \int_0^a e^{-x^2} dx = \int_0^a e^{-y^2} dy. \text{ Hence,}$$

$$I_a^2 = \int_0^a e^{-x^2} dx \int_0^a e^{-y^2} dy = \int_0^a \int_0^a e^{-(x^2+y^2)} dx\ dy.$$

(b) We are given that R is the region $0 \le \theta \le \frac{\pi}{2}$, $0 \le r \le$

Let S be the region outside R but inside the square $0 \le x \le a$, $0 \le y \le a$. Note that the area of S is $a^2 - \frac{\pi}{4} a^2 = (\frac{4-\pi}{4})a^2$, and that the maximum value of $e^{-x^2-y^2}$ on S is e^{-a^2}.

$$\left|I_a^2 - J_a\right| = \iint\limits_S e^{-(x^2+y^2)} dA \leq \left(\frac{4-\pi}{4}\right) a^2 e^{-a^2}$$

(c) $\quad J_a = \int_0^{\pi/2} \int_0^a e^{-r^2} r \, dr \, d\theta = \frac{\pi}{2}\left(-\frac{1}{2} e^{-r^2}\right)\Big|_0^a$

$$= \frac{\pi}{4}\left(1 - e^{-a^2}\right)$$

(d) $\quad \lim\limits_{a \to +\infty} (J_a) = \lim\limits_{a \to +\infty} \left[\frac{\pi}{4}\left(1-e^{-a^2}\right)\right] = \frac{\pi}{4}$

$$\lim\limits_{a \to +\infty} \left|(I_a^2 - J_a)\right| \leq \left(\frac{4-\pi}{4}\right) \lim\limits_{a \to +\infty} \left(a^2 e^{-a^2}\right) = 0$$

[Use L'Hospital's Rule on $\lim\limits_{a \to +\infty} \left(a^2 e^{-a^2}\right)$]

Hence, $\quad \int_0^{+\infty} \int_0^{+\infty} e^{-(x^2+y^2)} dx \, dy = \lim\limits_{a \to +\infty} (I_a^2) = \frac{\pi}{4}$

Adding three similar integrals from the other quadrants,

$$\int_{-\infty}^{+\infty} \int_{-\infty}^{+\infty} e^{-(x^2+y^2)} dx \, dy = \pi, \quad \text{or} \quad \left(\int_{-\infty}^{+\infty} e^{-x^2} dx\right)^2 = \pi,$$

or $\quad \int_{-\infty}^{+\infty} e^{-x^2} dx = \sqrt{\pi}$

Chapter Nineteen

Exercise 1, pp. 1022-1023

3. If $x = \cos t$ and $y = \cos t$, then $\dfrac{dx}{dt} = \dfrac{dy}{dt} = -\sin t$,

and $ds = \sqrt{\sin^2 t + \sin^2 t} \, dt = \sqrt{2} \sin t \, dt$. Hence,

$$\int_C x^2 y \, ds = \sqrt{2} \int_0^{\pi/2} \cos^3 t \sin t \, dt = \dfrac{-\sqrt{2}}{4} \cos^4 t \Big|_0^{\pi/2}$$

$$= -\dfrac{\sqrt{2}}{4}(0-1) = \dfrac{\sqrt{2}}{4}$$

7. (a) If $y = x^2$, then $dy = 2x \, dx$. Hence,

$$\int_C [(x+2y)\,dx + (2x+y)\,dy]$$

$$= \int_0^1 [(x+2x^2) + (2x+x^2)(2x)]\,dx = \int_0^1 (2x^3+6x^2+x)\,dx$$

$$= (\tfrac{1}{2} x^4 + 2x^3 + \tfrac{1}{2} x^2)\Big|_0^1 = \tfrac{1}{2} + 2 + \tfrac{1}{2} = 3$$

(b) If $y = x^3$, then $dy = 3x^2 \, dx$. Hence,

$$\int_C [(x+2y)\,dx + (2x+y)\,dy]$$

$$= \int_0^1 [(x+2x^3) + (2x+x^3)(3x^2)]\,dx = \int_0^1 (3x^5+8x^3+x)\,dx$$

$$= (\tfrac{1}{2} x^6 + 2x^4 + \tfrac{1}{2} x^2)\Big|_0^1 = \tfrac{1}{2} + 2 + \tfrac{1}{2} = 3$$

(c) If $x = \cos t$ and $y = \sin t$, then
$dx = -\sin t \, dt$ and $dy = \cos t \, dt$. Hence,

$$\int_C [x+2y)\,dx + (2x+y)\,dy]$$

$$= \int_0^{\pi/2} [(\cos t + 2 \sin t)(-\sin t)$$

$$+ (2 \cos t + \sin t)(\cos t)]dt$$

$$= \int_0^{\pi/2} (2 \cos^2 t - 2 \sin^2 t)dt = \int_0^{\pi/2} 2 \cos 2t \, dt$$

$$= \sin 2t \Big|_0^{\pi/2} = 0$$

(d) If $x = 1 - t$ and $y = t$, then $dx = -dt$ and $dy = dt$. Hence,

$$\int_C [(x+2y)dx + (2x+y)dy]$$

$$= \int_0^1 [(1-t+2t)(-1) + (2-2t+t)]dt = \int_0^1 (1-2t)dt$$

$$= (t-t^2) \Big|_0^1 = 0$$

11. We have $\int_C = \int_{C_1} + \int_{C_2} + \int_{C_3}$ with curves

C_1, C_2, C_3 defined as follows: on C_1 we have
$x = t$, $y = 0$, $0 \leq t \leq 1$; on C_2, $x = 1$, $y = t$,
$0 \leq t \leq 1$; on C_3, $x = 1 - t$, $y = 1$, $0 \leq t \leq 1$,
and $dx = -dt$. Hence,

$$\int_{C_1} [(x \cos y)dx - (y \sin x)dy] = \int_0^1 (t \, dt)$$

$$= \frac{1}{2} t^2 \Big|_0^1 = \frac{1}{2}$$

$$\int_{C_2} [(x \cos y)dx - (y \sin x)dy]$$

$$= \int_0^1 [\cos t(0) - t \sin 1 \, dt] = -\sin 1(\frac{1}{2} t^2) \Big|_0^1$$

$$= -\frac{1}{2} \sin 1$$

$\int_{C_3} [(x \cos y) dx - (y \sin x) dy]$

$= \int_0^1 [(1-t) \cos 1(-dt) - \sin(1-t)(0)]$

$= -\cos 1 \int_0^1 (1-t) dt = -\cos 1(t - \frac{1}{2} t^2)\Big|_0^1$

$= -\cos 1(1 - \frac{1}{2}) = -\frac{1}{2} \cos 1$

We conclude that $\int_C = \frac{1}{2} - \frac{1}{2}(\sin 1) - \frac{1}{2} \cos 1$

$= \frac{1}{2}(1 - \sin 1 - \cos 1)$

15. If $x = t^3$, $y = t$, and $z = t^2$, then $dx = 3t^2$, $dy = dt$, and $dz = 2t \, dt$. Hence,

$\int_C [(\frac{yz}{x}) dx + e^y dy + \sin z \, dz]$

$= \int_2^3 (3t^2 + e^t + 2t \sin t^2) dt = (t^3 + e^t - \cos t^2)\Big|_2^3$

$= (27-8) + (e^3 - e^2) - (\cos 9 - \cos 4)$

$= 19 + e^3 - e^2 - \cos 9 + \cos 4$

19. $\int_C = \int_{C_1} + \int_{C_2} + \int_{C_3} + \int_{C_4}$, where C_1, C_2, C_3, and C_4 can be defined as follows; C_1: $x = t$, $y = 0$, $z = 0$, $0 \leq t \leq 1$; C_2: $x = 1$, $y = t$, $z = 0$, $0 \leq t \leq 2$; C_3: $x = 1$, $y = 2$, $z = t$, $0 \leq t \leq 1$; and C_4: $x = 1 - t$, $y = 2 - 2t$, $z = 1$, $0 \leq t \leq 1$. Then we have

$\int_{C_1} [y z \, dx + (y + zx) dy + x z \, dz] = \int_0^1 0 \, dt = 0;$

$\int_{C_2} = \int_0^2 t \, dt = \frac{1}{2} t^2\Big|_0^2 = 2;$

$$\int_{C_3} = \int_0^1 t \ dt = \frac{1}{2} t^2 \Big|_0^1 = \frac{1}{2} \ ; \quad \text{and}$$

$$\int_{C_4} = \int_0^1 [(2-2t)(-1) + [(2-2t) + (1-t)](-2)] dt$$

$$= \int_0^1 (8t-8) dt = (4t^2-8t) \Big|_0^1 = 4 - 8 = -4.$$

Hence, $\int_C = 0 + 2 + \frac{1}{2} - 4 = -\frac{3}{2}$.

23. If $x = a \sin t$ and $y = b \cos t$, then $dx = a \cos t \ dt$ and $dy = -b \sin t \ dt$. Hence,

$$\int_C (y^n dx + x^n dy) = \int_0^{2\pi} (ab^n \cos^{n+1} t - a^n b \sin^{n+1} t) dt$$

$$= \frac{ab^n}{n+1} \cos^n t \sin t \Big|_0^{2\pi}$$

$$+ \frac{ab^n n}{n+1} \int_0^{2\pi} \cos^{n-1} t \ dt$$

$$+ \frac{a^n b}{n+1} \sin^n t \cos t \Big|_0^{2\pi}$$

$$- \frac{a^n b n}{n+1} \int_0^{2\pi} \sin^{n-1} t \ dt$$

$$= \frac{n}{n+1} [ab^n \int_0^{2\pi} \cos^{n-1} t \ dt$$

$$- a^n b \int_0^{2\pi} \sin^{n-1} t \ dt]$$

$$= \frac{n}{n+1} [\frac{ab^n}{n-1} \cos^{n-2} t \sin t \Big|_0^{2\pi}$$

$$+ \frac{ab^n (n-2)}{n-1} \int_0^{2\pi} \cos^{n-3} t \ dt$$

$$+ \frac{a^n b}{n-1} \sin^{n-2} t \cos t \Big|_0^{2\pi}$$

$$- \frac{a^n b (n-2)}{n-1} \int_0^{2\pi} \sin^{n-3} t \ dt]$$

$$= \left(\frac{n}{n+1}\right)\left(\frac{n-2}{n-1}\right)[ab^n \int_0^{2\pi} \cos^{n-3}t \; dt$$

$$- a^n b \int_0^{2\pi} \sin^{n-3}t \; dt]$$

and so on, using the integral formulas in the back of the text.

If n is even, then the formula reduces to

$$\int_C (y^n dx + x^n dy) = \left(\frac{n}{n+1}\right)\left(\frac{n-2}{n-1}\right)\cdots\left(\frac{4}{5}\right)\left(\frac{2}{3}\right)(ab^n \int_0^{2\pi} \cos t \; dt$$

$$- a^n b \int_0^{2\pi} \sin t \; dt) = 0$$

since $\int_0^{2\pi} \cos t \; dt = \int_0^{2\pi} \sin t \; dt = 0.$

If n is odd, then the formula reduces to

$$\int_C (y^n dx + x^n dy) = \left(\frac{n}{n+1}\right)\left(\frac{n-2}{n-1}\right)\cdots\left(\frac{3}{4}\right)\left(\frac{1}{2}\right)[ab^n \int_0^{2\pi} dt$$

$$- a^n b \int_0^{2\pi} dt]$$

$$= 2\pi\left(\frac{n}{n+1}\right)\left(\frac{n-2}{n-1}\right)\cdots\left(\frac{3}{4}\right)\left(\frac{1}{2}\right)(ab^n - a^n b)$$

$$= 2\pi ab[\left(\frac{1}{2}\right)\left(\frac{3}{4}\right)\cdots\left(\frac{n-2}{n-1}\right)\left(\frac{n}{n+1}\right)](b^{n-1} - a^{n-1})$$

27. We have $x = t$ and $y = t^2$, $d\vec{r} = (\vec{i} + 2t\vec{j})dt$, and $\vec{F}(x,y) = (t + 2t^2)\vec{i} + (2t + t^2)\vec{j}$. Hence,
$\vec{F} \cdot d\vec{r} = [(t + 2t^2) + (4t^2 + 2t^3)]dt$, or
$\vec{F} \cdot d\vec{r} = (2t^3 + 6t^2 + t)dt$. This gives

$$\int_C \vec{F} \cdot d\vec{r} = \int_0^1 (2t^3 + 6t^2 + t)dt = \left(\frac{1}{2}t^4 + 2t^3 + \frac{1}{2}t^2\right)\Big|_0^1$$

$$= \frac{1}{2} + 2 + \frac{1}{2} = 3$$

3. $\frac{\partial}{\partial y}(xe^y) = xe^y = \frac{\partial}{\partial x}(\frac{1}{2}x^2e^y)$. Since these two partial
derivatives agree everywhere in the plane, there is a
function whose gradient is $xe^y\vec{i} + \frac{1}{2}x^2e^y\vec{j}$ everywhere in
the plane.

7. (a) Let $P(x,y) = x^2 + 3y$ and $Q(x,y) = 3x$. Then $\frac{\partial P}{\partial y} = 3$
    and $\frac{\partial Q}{\partial x} = 3$. Since P, Q, $\frac{\partial P}{\partial y}$ and $\frac{\partial Q}{\partial x}$ are all
    continuous in the entire plane and since
    $\frac{\partial P}{\partial y} = \frac{\partial Q}{\partial x}$ in the same region, there is by (19.20)
    a function f such that $\vec{\nabla}f(x,y) = (x^2+3y)\vec{i} + 3x\vec{j}$.
    From (19.14), the integral is independent of path.

    (b) Since $\vec{\nabla}f(x,y) = (x^2+3y)\vec{i} + 3x\vec{j}$, we need to find a
    function f so that $\frac{\partial f}{\partial x} = x^2 + 3y$ and $\frac{\partial f}{\partial y} = 3x$.

    Let $f(x,y) = \int(x^2+3y)dx + g(y) = \frac{x^3}{3} + 3xy + g(y)$.

    Then $\frac{\partial f}{\partial y}(x,y) = 3x + g'(y)$. Comparison of this

    with $\frac{\partial f}{\partial y}(x,y) = 3x$ requires $g(y) = 0$. If we let

    $g(y) = 0$, we have $f(x,y) = \frac{x^3}{3} + 3xy$ as a function

    whose gradient is $(x^2+3y)\vec{i} + 3x\vec{j}$.

    (c) $\int_c[(x^2+3xy)dx + 3x\ dy] = f(x,y)\Big|_{(1,2)}^{(-3,5)}$

    $= (\frac{x^3}{3}+3xy)\Big|_{(1,2)}^{(-3,5)} = (-9 - 45) - (\frac{1}{3}+6) = -\frac{181}{3}$

11. Using $\frac{\partial f}{\partial x}(x,y) = 3x^2y^2$, we have $f(x,y) = x^3y^2 + g(y)$.

This gives $\frac{\partial f}{\partial y}(x,y) = 2x^3y + g'(y)$. Comparison of this

with $\frac{\partial f}{\partial y}(x,y) = 2x^3y$ gives $g'(y) = 0$. If we let $g(y) = 0$,

we have $f(x,y) = x^3y^2$ as a function whose gradient is
$3x^2y^2\vec{i} + 2x^3y\vec{j}$.

15. Using $\frac{\partial f}{\partial x}(x,y) = 2xy - y^2$, we have $f(x,y)$

$= x^2y - xy^2 + g(y)$. This gives $\frac{\partial f}{\partial y}(x,y)$

$= x^2 - 2xy + g'(y)$. Comparison of this with $\frac{\partial f}{\partial y}(x,y)$

$= x^2 - 2xy$ gives $g'(y) = 0$. If we let $g(y) = 0$, we

have $f(x,y) = x^2y - xy^2$ as a function with the desired
gradient.

19. Using $\frac{\partial f}{\partial x}(x,y) = y \cos(x) - 2 \sin(y)$, we have $f(x,y)$

$= y \sin(x) - 2x \sin(y) + g(y)$. This gives $\frac{\partial f}{\partial y}(x,y)$

$= \sin(x) - 2x \cos(y) + g'(y)$. Comparison of this

with $\frac{\partial f}{\partial y}(x,y) = -[2x \cos(x) - \sin(x)]$ gives $g'(y) = 0$.

If we let $g(y) = 0$, we have $f(x,y) = y \sin(x)$
$- 2x \sin(y)$ as a function with the required gradient.

23. Since $\frac{\partial}{\partial y}(\frac{-y}{x^2+y^2}) = \frac{y^2 - x^2}{(x^2+y^2)^2} = \frac{\partial}{\partial x}(\frac{x}{x^2+y^2})$ in any region

which does not contain the origin and since the
rectangle R does not contain the origin as long as a
is positive, we can conclude that the integral is
independent of the curve C in R.

Let $\frac{\partial f}{\partial x}(x,y) = \frac{-y}{x^2 + y^2}$, then $f(x,y) = \text{Arctan}(\frac{y}{x}) + g(y)$.

Thus $\frac{\partial f}{\partial y}(x,y) = \frac{x}{x^2 + y^2} + g'(y)$. Comparing this with

$\frac{\partial f}{\partial y}(x,y) = \frac{x}{x^2 + y^2}$ we need $g'(y) = 0$. Letting

$g(y) = 0$ we have $f(x,y) = \text{Arctan}\left(\frac{y}{x}\right)$ as a function such that $\vec{\nabla}f(x,y) = (-y\vec{i}+x\vec{j})/(x^2+y^2)$.

Exercise 3, p. 1041

3. If $\vec{r}(t) = (3 \cos t)\vec{i} + (2 \sin t)\vec{j}$, then $x = 3 \cos t$, $y = 2 \sin t$, $d\vec{r} = (-3 \sin t)\vec{i} + (2 \cos t)\vec{j}$, and $\vec{F} = (3 \cos t - 4 \sin t)\vec{i} + 6 \sin t \cos t\ \vec{j}$. Hence,

$$\int_C \vec{F} \cdot d\vec{r} = \int_0^{\pi/2} (-9 \sin t \cos t + 12 \sin^2 t$$

$$+ 12 \sin t \cos^2 t)dt$$

$$= -\frac{9}{2} \int_0^{\pi/2} \sin 2t\ dt + 6 \int_0^{\pi/2} (1 - \cos 2t)dt$$

$$- 12 \int_0^{\pi/2} \cos^2 t(-\sin t\ dt)$$

$$= \frac{9}{4} \cos 2t \Big|_0^{\pi/2} + (6t - 3 \sin 2t)\Big|_0^{\pi/2} - 4 \cos^3 t \Big|_0^{\pi/2}$$

$$= \frac{9}{4}(\cos \pi - \cos 0) + 3\pi - 4(\cos^3 \tfrac{\pi}{2} - \cos^3 0)$$

$$= \frac{9}{4}(-1 - 1) + 3\pi - 4(0-1) = 3\pi + 4 - \frac{9}{2} = 3\pi - \frac{1}{2}$$

7. Letting $x = \cos t$, $y = \sin t$, $0 \le t \le \pi$, we have $\vec{r}(t) = (\cos t)\vec{i} + (\sin t)\vec{j}$, so that $\vec{F}(t) = (\sin t - \cos^2 t)\vec{i} + (\cos t)\vec{j}$ and $d\vec{r} = (-\sin t)\vec{i} + (\cos t)\vec{j}$. Hence,

$$\int_C \vec{F} \cdot d\vec{r} = \int_0^\pi (-\sin^2 t + \cos^2 t \sin t + \cos^2 t)dt$$

$$= \int_0^\pi \cos^2 t \sin t\ dt + \int_0^\pi (\cos^2 t - \sin^2 t)dt$$

$$= -\frac{1}{3} \cos^3 t \Big|_0^\pi + \int_0^\pi \cos 2t\ dt$$

$$= (-\frac{1}{3} \cos^3 t + \frac{1}{2} \sin 2t)\Big|_0^\pi$$

$$= -\frac{1}{3}(-1 \ -1) + \frac{1}{2}(0 \ - \ 0) = \frac{2}{3}$$

11. Choose C_1 to be the path along $y = x$ for $0 \le x \le 1$. Then $\vec{r} = x\vec{i} + x\vec{j}$, so that $\vec{dr} = (\vec{i} + \vec{j})dx$. Then, with $\vec{F} = y\vec{i} - x\vec{j} = x\vec{i} - x\vec{j}$, we have

$$\int_{C_1} \vec{F} \cdot \vec{dr} = \int_0^1 (x-x)dx = \int_0^1 0 \ dx = 0$$

If we take the x-axis from $(0,0)$ to $(1,0)$, then use $x = t$, $y = 0$, $0 \le t \le 1$, for C_2. Hence, $\vec{F} = y\vec{i} - x\vec{j} = -t\vec{j}$, $\vec{r}(t) = t\vec{i} + 0\vec{j}$, and $\vec{dr} = \vec{i}dt$. Thus, $\vec{F} \cdot \vec{dr} = 0$ and $\int_{C_2} \vec{F} \cdot \vec{dr} = 0$. From $(1,0)$ to $(1,1)$, we let $x = 1$, $y = t$, $0 \le t \le 1$ for C_3. Then, $\vec{F} = y\vec{i} - x\vec{j} = t\vec{i} - \vec{j}$, $\vec{r}(t) = \vec{i} + t\vec{j}$, and $\vec{dr} = \vec{j}dt$. Hence, $\int_{C_3} \vec{F} \cdot \vec{dr} = \int_0^1 -dt = -t\Big|_0^1 = -1$. This gives $\int_C \vec{F} \cdot \vec{dr} = \int_{C_2} \vec{F} \cdot \vec{dr} + \int_{C_3} \vec{F} \cdot \vec{dr} = -1$.

Since the different paths give different results, we conclude that $\vec{F}$ is nonconservative.

15. Denote the line segment from $(1,0)$ to $(-1,2)$ by C and use for a parameterization, $x = 1 - t$, $y = t$, $0 \le t \le 2$. Then $\vec{r}(t) = (1-t)\vec{i} + t\vec{j}$, $0 \le t \le 2$. On C we have $\vec{F}(x(t),y(t)) = \dfrac{1 - t}{(1-2t+2t^2)^{3/2}}\vec{i}$

$+ \dfrac{t}{(1-2t+2t^2)^{3/2}}\vec{j}$ and $\vec{dr} = (-\vec{i}+\vec{j})dt$. The work done in moving the particle Q along this path is

$$\int_C \vec{F} \cdot \vec{dr} = \int_0^2 \frac{-1 + 2t}{(1-2t+2t^2)^{3/2}} \ dt = \frac{1}{2} \int_1^5 \frac{du}{u^{3/2}}$$

$$= -u^{-\frac{1}{2}}\Big|_1^5 = 1 - \frac{\sqrt{5}}{5} \text{ units of work.}$$

3. We have $p = xy$ and $q = x + y$, so that

$\dfrac{\partial p}{\partial y} = x$ and $\dfrac{\partial q}{\partial x} = 1$. Hence,

$\oint_C [xy\ dx + (x+y)dy] = \iint_R (1-x)dx\ dy = \int_0^3 \int_0^4 (1-x)dx\ dy$

$= (x - \dfrac{1}{2}x^2)\Big|_0^4 \int_0^3 dy$

$= (4-8)(y)\Big|_0^3 = -12$

7. Using $p = -x^2 y$ and $q = y^2 x$ gives $\dfrac{\partial q}{\partial x} = y^2$ and

$\dfrac{\partial p}{\partial y} = -x^2$. Hence, $\dfrac{\partial q}{\partial x} - \dfrac{\partial p}{\partial y} = x^2 + y^2$, and we have

$\oint_C (-x^2 y\ dx + y^2 x\ dy) = \iint_R (x^2+y^2)dx\ dy$

$= 4 \int_0^1 \int_0^{\sqrt{1-x^2}} (x^2+y^2)dy\ dx$

$= 4 \int_0^1 [(x^2 y + \dfrac{1}{3}y^3)\Big|_0^{\sqrt{1-x^2}}]dx$

$= 4 \int_0^1 x^2\sqrt{1-x^2}\ dx$

$+ \dfrac{4}{3}\int_0^1 (1-x^2)^{3/2}dx$

(Let $x = \sin\theta \Rightarrow \sqrt{1-x^2}$

$= \cos\theta$ and $dx = \cos\theta\ d\theta$;

$x = 0 \Rightarrow \theta = 0$, and $x = 1$

$\Rightarrow \theta = \dfrac{\pi}{2}$.)

$= \int_0^{\pi/2} 4\sin^2\theta\ \cos^2\theta\ d\theta$

$+ \dfrac{4}{3}\int_0^{\pi/2} \cos^4\theta\ d\theta$

$$= \int_0^{\pi/2} \sin^2 2\theta \, d\theta$$

$$+ \frac{1}{3} \int_0^{\pi/2} (1 + \cos 2\theta)^2 d\theta$$

$$= \frac{1}{2} \int_0^{\pi/2} (1 - \cos 4\theta) d\theta$$

$$+ \frac{1}{3} \int_0^{\pi/2} (1 + 2 \cos 2\theta$$

$$+ \frac{1}{2} + \frac{1}{2} \cos 4\theta) d\theta$$

$$= \int_0^{\pi/2} d\theta + \frac{2}{3} \int_0^{\pi/2} \cos 2\theta \, d\theta$$

$$- \frac{1}{3} \int_0^{\pi/2} \cos 4\theta \, d\theta$$

$$= \frac{\pi}{2} + \frac{1}{3} \sin 2\theta \Big|_0^{\pi/2} - \frac{1}{12} \sin 4\theta \Big|_0^{\pi/2}$$

$$= \frac{\pi}{2}$$

11. If $p = x^2 + y$ and $q = x - y^2$, then $\frac{\partial q}{\partial x} = 1$ and $\frac{\partial p}{\partial y} = 1$. Hence,

$$\oint_C [(x^2+y) dx + (x-y^2) dy] = \iint_R \left(\frac{\partial q}{\partial x} - \frac{\partial p}{\partial y}\right) dx \, dy$$

$$= \iint_R 0 \, dx \, dy = 0$$

15. If $p = \frac{1}{y}$ and $q = \frac{1}{x}$,

then $\frac{\partial q}{\partial x} = \frac{-1}{x^2}$, $\frac{\partial p}{\partial y} = \frac{-1}{y^2}$,

and $\frac{\partial q}{\partial x} - \frac{\partial p}{\partial y} = \frac{1}{y^2} - \frac{1}{x^2}$.

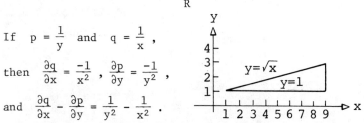

We have $\oint_C p\,dx + q\,dy = \iint_R (y^{-2} - x^{-2})\,dx\,dy$

$$= \int_1^9 \int_1^{\sqrt{x}} (y^{-2} - x^{-2})\,dy\,dx$$

$$= \int_1^9 [(-\frac{1}{y} - \frac{y}{x^2})\big|_1^{\sqrt{x}}]\,dx$$

$$= \int_1^9 [(\frac{-1}{\sqrt{x}} - \frac{\sqrt{x}}{x^2}) - (-1 - \frac{1}{x^2})]\,dx$$

$$= \int_1^9 (1 + x^{-2} - x^{-1/2} - x^{-3/2})\,dx$$

$$= (x - \frac{1}{x} - 2\sqrt{x} + \frac{2}{\sqrt{x}})\big|_1^9$$

$$= (9 - \frac{1}{9} - 6 + \frac{2}{3}) - (1 - 1 - 2 + 2)$$

$$= 3 - \frac{1}{9} + \frac{2}{3} = \frac{27 - 1 + 6}{9} = \frac{32}{9}$$

19. We have $A = \oint_C x\,dy = \oint_{C_1} x\,dy - \oint_{C_2} x\,dy$, where C_1

is the x-axis, $0 \le x \le 2\pi$, and C_2 is defined by
$\vec{r}(t)$. If $\vec{r}(t) = (2\pi t - \sin 2\pi t)\vec{i} + (1 - \cos 2\pi t)\vec{j}$,
then $x = 2\pi t - \sin 2\pi t$ and $y = 1 - \cos 2\pi t$. This
gives $dy = 2\pi \sin 2\pi t\,dt$ and hence,

$$\oint_{C_2} x\,dy = \int_0^1 (2\pi t - \sin 2\pi t)(2\pi \sin 2\pi t)\,dt$$

$$= 2\pi \int_0^1 2\pi t \sin 2\pi t\,dt - 2\pi \int_0^1 \sin^2 2\pi t\,dt$$

(Let $u = t$; $du = dt$; $dv = 2\pi \sin 2\pi t\,dt$;
$v = -\cos 2\pi t$.)

$$= (-2\pi t \cos 2\pi t)\big|_0^1 + 2\pi \int_0^1 \cos 2\pi t\,dt$$

$$- \pi \int_0^1 (1 - \cos 4\pi t)\,dt$$

$$= -2\pi + \sin 2\pi t \Big|_0^1 - \pi(t - \frac{1}{4\pi} \sin 4\pi t)\Big|_0^1 = -3\pi$$

Also, C_1 is defined by $y = 0$, $0 \le x \le 2\pi$, so that

$$\oint_{C_1} x\,dy = \int_0^{2\pi} x(0)\,dx = 0$$

Hence, $A = \oint_C x\,dy = \oint_{C_1} x\,dy - \oint_{C_2} x\,dy = 0 - (-3\pi) = 3\pi$

23. We have $\oint_C p\,dx + q\,dy$ with $p = e^x \sin y$ and
$q = e^x \cos y$. This gives $\frac{\partial q}{\partial x} = e^x \cos y$ and
$\frac{\partial p}{\partial y} = e^x \cos y$. Since $\frac{\partial q}{\partial x} = \frac{\partial p}{\partial y}$ in the simply
connected region enclosed by C, we have
$\oint_C p\,dx + q\,dy = 0$.

27. The hypocycloid C_1: $x^{2/3} + y^{2/3} = 1$ lies interior
to the circle C_2: $x^2 + y^2 = 4$, which was considered
in Problem 25. In the region interior to the circle
and outside the hypocycloid, p and q have
continuous partial derivatives and $\frac{\partial p}{\partial y} = \frac{\partial q}{\partial x}$ in any
open connected set with the point $(0,0)$ deleted.
Hence, $\oint_{C_1} = \oint_{C_2} = -2\pi$, as was shown in Problem 25.

31. We know from (19.52) that the area of the region
is expressible as $A = \frac{1}{2} \oint_C (-y\,dx + x\,dy)$. To evaluate
this line integral we decompose the boundry of the
region into three curves.
C_1: The line segment from $(0,0)$ to
$\quad\quad (f(\alpha) \cos \alpha, f(\alpha) \sin (\alpha))$.
C_2: The graph of f for $\alpha \le \theta < \beta$, i.e.
$\quad\quad (f(\theta) \cos (\theta), f(\theta) \sin (\theta)), \alpha \le \theta \le \beta$.

C_3: The line segment from $(f(\beta) \cos (\beta), f(\beta) \sin (\beta))$ to $(0,0)$.

Then $A = \frac{1}{2}\int_{C_1} (-ydx+xdy) + \frac{1}{2}\int_{C_2} (-ydx+xdy)$

$+ \frac{1}{2}\int_{C_3} (-ydx + xdy)$.

Consider the first integral. We describe the curve C_1 by $\vec{r}(t) = t\vec{i} + t \tan (\alpha)\vec{j}$, $0 \le t \le f(\alpha) \cos (\alpha)$. Then on C_1 $\vec{F}(x,y) = -y\vec{i} + x\vec{j}$ has the value $\vec{F}(t)$ $= -t \tan (\alpha)\vec{i} + t\vec{j}$ and $d\vec{r} = (\vec{i} + \tan (\alpha)\vec{j})dt$. Consequently, $\vec{F}\cdot d\vec{r} = (-t \tan (\alpha) + t \tan (\alpha))dt = 0dt$. Therefore the first integral contributes nothing towards the sum. Likewise the third integral has a value of zero. To see this, let $\vec{r}(t) = -t\vec{i} - t \tan(\beta)\vec{j}$, $- f(\beta) \cos (\beta) \le t \le 0$ and follow the procedure that we just used. To evaluate the second integral, describe the curve C_2 by $\vec{r}(t) = f(t) \cos (t)\vec{i}$ $+ f(t) \sin (t)\vec{j}$, $\alpha \le t \le \beta$. On C_2 we have $\vec{F}(t)$ $= -f(t) \sin (t) \vec{i} + f(t) \cos (t)\vec{j}$ and $d\vec{r} =$ $\{(f'(t) \cos (t) - f(t) \sin (t)]\vec{i} + [f'(t) \sin (t)$ $+ f(t) \cos (t)]\vec{j}\}dt$. Thus $\vec{F}\cdot d\vec{r} = [f^2(t) \sin^2(t)$ $+ f^2(t) \cos^2(t)]dt = f^2(t)dt$. Putting this all together we have

$A = \frac{1}{2} \oint_C(-ydx+xdy) = \frac{1}{2} \int_{C_3} (-ydx+xdy) = \frac{1}{2} \int_\alpha^\beta f^2(t)dt$.

Exercise 5, p. 1056

3. Using $f(x,y) = z = 2 - \frac{1}{2} x - \frac{1}{2} y$ gives $f_x = -\frac{1}{2}$, $f_y = -\frac{1}{2}$, and $\sqrt{f_x^2 + f_y^2 + 1}$

$= \sqrt{\frac{3}{2}} = \frac{\sqrt{6}}{2}$. With $\emptyset(x,y,z)$

$= x$, we have

$$\iint\limits_{\Sigma} \emptyset(x,y,z)\,dS = \iint\limits_{R} (x)\,\frac{\sqrt{6}}{2}\,dx\,dy = \frac{\sqrt{6}}{2}\int_0^1 x \int_0^1 dy\,dx$$

$$= \frac{\sqrt{6}}{2}\int_0^1 x\,dx = \frac{\sqrt{6}}{4}\,x^2\Big|_0^1 = \frac{\sqrt{6}}{4}$$

7. We will consider the portion of
the cylinder $y = f(x,z) = \sqrt{1 - x^2}$
for $0 \le x \le 1$ and its
projection on the xz-plane for
$0 \le z \le 1$. We then have

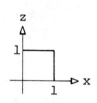

$$f_x = \frac{-x}{\sqrt{1 - x^2}}\ ,\ f_z = 0,\ \sqrt{f_x^2 + f_z^2 + 1} = \sqrt{\frac{x^2}{1-x^2} + 1}$$

$$= \frac{1}{\sqrt{1 - x^2}}\ ,\quad \text{and}\quad \iint\limits_{\Sigma} \emptyset(x,y,z)\,dS = \iint\limits_{R} \frac{x^2}{\sqrt{1 - x^2}}\,dx\,dz$$

$$= \int_0^1 \int_0^1 \frac{x^2}{\sqrt{1 - x^2}}\,dz\,dx = \int_0^1 \frac{x^2}{\sqrt{1 - x^2}}\,[z\Big|_0^1]dx = \int_0^1 \frac{x^2}{\sqrt{1 - x^2}}\,dx$$

$$= \int_0^{\pi/2} \frac{\sin^2\theta}{\cos\theta}\,\cos\theta\,d\theta = \int_0^{\pi/2} (\frac{1}{2} - \frac{1}{2}\cos 2\theta)d\theta$$

$$= \frac{1}{2}\,\theta - \frac{1}{4}\,\sin 2\theta\Big|_0^{\pi/2} = \frac{\pi}{4}$$

Exercise 6, p. 1063

3. Use $\vec{F} = z\vec{i}$, decompose S into its six faces, and
evaluate over each face:

Face	$\vec{n}$	$\vec{F} \cdot \vec{n}$	$\rho\iint\limits_{\Sigma} \vec{F} \cdot \vec{n}\ dS$
Σ_1: $z = 0$	$-\vec{k}$	0	0
Σ_2: $y = 0$	$-\vec{j}$	0	0
Σ_3: $x = 0$	$-\vec{i}$	$-z$	$-\rho\iint\limits_{\Sigma} z\,dS = -\rho\int_0^1 \int_0^1 z\,dy\,dz$

$$= -\frac{\rho}{2}$$

Face	$\vec{n}$	$\vec{F} \cdot \vec{n}$	$\rho\iint\limits_{\Sigma} \vec{F} \cdot \vec{n} \, dS$

Σ_4: x = 1 $\vec{i}$ z $\rho\iint\limits_{\Sigma} z\,dS = \rho\int_0^1 \int_0^1 z \, dy \, dz$

$$= \rho/2$$

Σ_5: y = 1 $\vec{j}$ 0   0

Σ_6: z = 1 $\vec{k}$ 0   0

The total fluid mass is $0 + 0 - \rho/2 + \rho/2 + 0 + 0 = 0.$

7. The outer unit normal $\vec{n}$ of the surface $f(x+y) = z = \sqrt{1-x^2-y^2}$ is

$$\vec{n} = \frac{-f_x\vec{i} - f_y\vec{j} + \vec{k}}{\sqrt{1 + f_x^2 + f_y^2}} = \frac{\frac{x}{z}\vec{i} + \frac{y}{z}\vec{j} + \vec{k}}{\sqrt{1 + \frac{x^2}{z^2} + \frac{y^2}{z^2}}} = \frac{x\vec{i} + y\vec{j} + z\vec{k}}{\sqrt{x^2 + y^2 + z^2}}$$

$= x\vec{i} + y\vec{j} + z\vec{k}.$ Therefore $\vec{F}\cdot\vec{n}$

$= (x\vec{i} + y\cdot\vec{j} + z\vec{k})\cdot(x\vec{i} + y\vec{j} + z\vec{k}) = x^2 + y^2 + z^2 = 1$

Thus, $\iint\limits_{\Sigma} \vec{F}\cdot\vec{n} \, ds = \iint\limits_{\Sigma} 1 \, ds = 2\pi$ (The surface area of a

a hemisphere of radius 1.)

1. The outer unit normal $\vec{n}$ of the surface $f(x,y) = z = 8 - 2x - 2y$

is $\vec{n} = \dfrac{-f_x\vec{i} - f_y\vec{j} + \vec{k}}{\sqrt{1 + f_x^2 + f_y^2}} = \dfrac{2\vec{i} + 2\vec{j} + \vec{k}}{\sqrt{1 + 4 + 4}} = \dfrac{2}{3}\vec{i} + \dfrac{2}{3}\vec{j} + \dfrac{1}{3}\vec{k}.$

Therefore, $\vec{F}\cdot\vec{n} = ((x+y)\vec{i} + (2x-z)\vec{j} + y\vec{k})\cdot(\dfrac{2}{3}\vec{i} + \dfrac{2}{3}\vec{j} + \dfrac{1}{3}\vec{k})$

$= 2x + y - \dfrac{2}{3}z = 2x + y - \dfrac{2}{3}(8-2x-2y) = \dfrac{10x + 7y - 16}{3}.$

Thus $\iint\limits_{\Sigma} \vec{F}\cdot\vec{n} \, ds = \iint\limits_{\Sigma} (\dfrac{10x+7y-16}{3})ds = \iint\limits_{R} (\dfrac{10x+7y-16}{3})3 \, dydx$

$= \int_0^4 \int_0^{4-x} (10x+7y-16)dydx = \int_0^4 (\dfrac{-13x^2}{2}+28x-8)dx = \dfrac{160}{3}.$

3.   If $\vec{F}(x,y,z) = (x+\cos(x))\vec{i} + (y+y\sin(x))\vec{j} + 27\vec{k}$,
then $\vec{\nabla}\cdot\vec{F}(x,y,z) = $ div $\vec{F}(x,y,z) = 1 - \sin(x) + 1$
$+ \sin(x) + 2 = 4$.

7.   If $\vec{F} = x^2\vec{i} + y^2\vec{j} + z^2\vec{k}$,   then   div $\vec{F} = 2x + 2y + 2z$.
The divergence theorem gives

$$\iint\limits_{S} \vec{F} \cdot \vec{n} \ dS = \iiint\limits_{T} (2x + 2y + 2z) dV$$

$$= \int_0^1 \int_0^1 \int_0^1 (2x + 2y + 2z) dz \ dy \ dx$$

$$= \int_0^1 \int_0^1 [2xz + 2yz + z^2 \Big|_0^1] dy \ dx$$

$$= \int_0^1 \int_0^1 (2x + 2y + 1) dy \ dx$$

$$= \int_0^1 [2xy + y^2 + y \Big|_0^1] dx$$

$$= \int_0^1 (2x + 2) dx = (x^2 + 2x) \Big|_0^1 = 3$$

11. If $\vec{F} = x^2\vec{i} + 2y\vec{j} + 4z^2\vec{k}$, then div $\vec{F} = 2x + 2 + 8z$.
The divergence theorem gives

$$\iint_S \vec{F} \cdot \vec{n} \, dS = \iiint_T (2x + 2 + 8z)\,dx\,dy\,dz$$

$$= 2 \int_{-2}^{2} \int_{y=0}^{\sqrt{4-x^2}} \int_{0}^{2} (2x + 2 + 8z)\,dz\,dy\,dz$$

$$= 2 \int_{-2}^{2} \int_{0}^{\sqrt{4-x^2}} [(2xz + 2z + 4z^2)\Big|_{0}^{2}]\,dy\,dx$$

$$= 2 \int_{-2}^{2} \int_{0}^{\sqrt{4-x^2}} (4x + 20)\,dy\,dx$$

$$= 2 \int_{-2}^{2} [(4x + 20)y\Big|_{0}^{\sqrt{4-x^2}}]\,dx$$

$$= 8 \int_{-2}^{2} (x + 5)\sqrt{4 - x^2}\,dx$$

$$= 8 \int_{-2}^{2} \sqrt{4 - x^2}(x\,dx) + 40 \int_{-2}^{2} \sqrt{4 - x^2}\,dx$$

$$= \frac{-16}{3}(4 - x^2)^{3/2}\Big|_{-2}^{2} + 40[\tfrac{1}{2}\pi(2)^2]$$

$$= (0-0) + 80\pi = 80\pi$$

15. If $\vec{F} = x^2\vec{i} + y^2\vec{j} + z^2\vec{k}$, then div $\vec{F} = 2x + 2y + 2z$.
The divergence theorem gives

$$\iint_S \vec{F} \cdot \vec{n} \, dS = 2 \iiint_T (x + y + z)\,dV$$

$$= 2 \int_{-q}^{q} \int_{-\sqrt{q^2-x^2}}^{\sqrt{q^2-x^2}} \int_{z=q-\sqrt{q^2-x^2-y^2}}^{q+\sqrt{q^2-x^2-y^2}} (x+y+z)\,dz\,dy\,dx$$

since T is the region enclosed by $x^2 + y^2 + (z-q)^2$
$= q^2$, or $z - q = \pm\sqrt{q^2 - x^2 - y^2}$. For convenience,
change to cylindrical coordinates, $x = r \cos \theta$,

$y = r \sin \theta$, $z = z$, and $dv = r\ dr\ d\theta\ dz$. This gives

$$\iint_S \vec{F} \cdot \vec{n}\ dS = \int_{r=0}^{q} \int_{\theta=0}^{2\pi} \int_{q-\sqrt{q^2-r^2}}^{q+\sqrt{q^2-r^2}} 2[r(\cos\theta + \sin\theta) + 2]$$

$$r\ dz\ d\theta\ dr$$

$$= \int_{r=0}^{q} \int_{0}^{2\pi} [2r^2(\cos\theta + \sin\theta)z$$

$$+ rz^2 \Big|_{q-\sqrt{q^2-r^2}}^{q+\sqrt{q^2-r^2}}\ ]d\theta\ dr$$

$$= \int_{0}^{q} \int_{0}^{2\pi} [4(\cos\theta + \sin\theta)r^2\sqrt{1-r^2}$$

$$+ 4rq\sqrt{q^2-r^2}]d\theta\ dr$$

$$= \int_{0}^{q} 4r^2\sqrt{1-r^2}[(\sin\theta - \cos\theta)\Big|_{0}^{2\pi}\ ]dr$$

$$+ 4q\int_{0}^{q} r\sqrt{q^2-r^2}[\theta\Big|_{0}^{2\pi}\ ]dr$$

$$= \int_{0}^{q} 4r^2\sqrt{1-r^2}[(0-1) - (0-1)]dr$$

$$+ 8\pi q \int_{0}^{q} \sqrt{q^2-r^2}(rdr)$$

$$= 0 - 4\pi q (\tfrac{2}{3})(q^2-r^2)^{3/2}\Big|_{0}^{q}$$

$$= 0 + \frac{8\pi q}{3}(q^2)^{3/2} = \frac{8\pi q^4}{3}$$

Note that in substituting the limits on z after integrating with respect to z, letting $b = \sqrt{q^2-r^2}$, we make use of the formula $[(q+b)^2 - (q-b)^2]$ $= q^2 + 2qb + b^2 - q^2 + 2qb - b^2 = 4qb$ and $[(q+b) - (q-b)] = 2b$.

19. The cone can be defined as the solution set of the equation

$G(x,y,z) = h^2x^2 + h^2y^2 - r^2t^2 = 0$, $z > 0$.

Then the outer unit normal $\vec{n} = \dfrac{\vec{\nabla}G}{||\vec{\nabla}G||}$. Since

$\vec{\nabla}G(x,y,z) = 2h^2x\ \vec{i} + 2h^2y\ \vec{j} - 2r^2z\ \vec{k}$ we have

$||\vec{\nabla}G|| = 2\sqrt{h^4x^2 + h^4y^2 + r^4z^2} = 2rz\sqrt{r^2 + h^2}$,

$(h^2x^2+h^2y^2 = r^2z^2)$.

Therefore $\vec{n} = \dfrac{h^2x}{2rz\sqrt{r^2+h^2}}\vec{i} + \dfrac{h^2y}{2rz\sqrt{r^2+h^2}}\vec{j} - \dfrac{r}{\sqrt{r^2+h^2}}\vec{k}$.

Now decompose the surface Σ of the cone into the three surfaces, Σ_1 the top $z = k$, Σ_2 the curved surface $y \geq 0$ and Σ_3 the curved surface $y < 0$.

Then on Σ_1 we have $\vec{n} = \vec{k}$ and $\vec{F} = x\vec{i} + y\vec{j} + h\vec{k}$.

$\vec{F}\cdot\vec{n} = h$ so $\iint\limits_{\Sigma_1} \vec{F}\cdot\vec{n}\ ds = \iint\limits_{R} h\ dy\,dx = 4h \int_0^r \int_0^{\sqrt{r^2\ x^2}} dy\,dx$

$= \pi r^2 h$.

On Σ_2 we replace y with $\dfrac{\sqrt{r^2z^2 - h^2x^2}}{h}$ in both $\vec{F}$ and $\vec{n}$ to get

$\vec{F}\cdot\vec{n} = (x\vec{i} + \dfrac{\sqrt{r^2z^2 - h^2x^2}}{h}\vec{j} + z\vec{k})$

$\qquad \cdot (\dfrac{h^2x\vec{i} + h\sqrt{r^2z^2 - h^2x^2}\vec{j} - 2r^2z\vec{k}}{2rz\sqrt{r^2 + h^2}})$

$\qquad = \dfrac{h^2x^2 + (r^2z^2 - h^2x^2) - 2r^2z^2}{2rz\sqrt{r^2 + h^2}} = \dfrac{-r^2z^2}{2rz\sqrt{r^2 + h^2}}$

$\qquad = \dfrac{-rz}{2\sqrt{r^2 + h^2}}$

This yields $\iint\limits_{\Sigma_2} \vec{F}\cdot\vec{n}\ ds = \iint\limits_{R} \dfrac{-rz}{2\sqrt{r^2 + h^2}}\ 2rz\sqrt{r^2 + h^2}\ dx\,dz$

$= \int_0^h \int_{\frac{-rz}{h}}^{\frac{rz}{h}} - r^2z^2\ dx\,dz = \int_0^h 0\ dz = 0$.

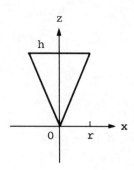

In a similar manner on Σ_3 we have, upon replacing

y with $\dfrac{-\sqrt{r^2z^2 - h^2x^2}}{h}$ in both $\vec{F}$ and $\vec{n}$, $\vec{F}\cdot\vec{n}$

$= \dfrac{-rz}{2\sqrt{r^2 + h^2}}$. Thus, $\iint\limits_{\Sigma_3} \vec{F}\cdot\vec{n}\ ds$

$= \iint\limits_{R} \dfrac{-rz}{2\sqrt{r^2 + h^2}}\ 2rz\sqrt{r^2 + h^2}\ dxdz = 0.$

Summing these three results gives us

$v = \dfrac{1}{3}\iint\limits_{\Sigma} \vec{F}\cdot\vec{n}\ ds = \dfrac{1}{3}[\pi r^2h + 0 + 0] = \dfrac{1}{3}\pi r^2h.$

23.   The outer unit normal $\vec{n} = \dfrac{2x\vec{i} + 2y\vec{j} + 27\vec{k}}{\sqrt{4x^2 + 4y^2 + 4z^2}}$

$= \dfrac{x\vec{i} + y\vec{j} + z\vec{k}}{10}$ by use of the fact that

$x^2 + y^2 + z^2 = 100.$ Therefore $\vec{F}\cdot\vec{n} = \dfrac{x^2 + y^2 + z^2}{10}$

$= \dfrac{100}{10} = 10.$ Thus $\iint\limits_{\Sigma} \vec{F}\cdot\vec{n}\ ds = \iint\limits_{\Sigma} 10ds = 10(4\pi r^2)$

$= 10(4\pi(100)) = 4000\pi.$

On the other hand we have $\vec{\nabla}\cdot\vec{F} = 1 + 1 + 1 = 3$ so

$\iiint\limits_{T} \vec{\nabla}\cdot\vec{F}\ dv = \iiint\limits_{T} 3\ dv = 3(\dfrac{4}{3}\pi r^3) = 4\pi(1000) = 4000\pi.$

3. If $\vec{F}(x,y,z) = xyz\vec{i} + xz\vec{j} + z\vec{k}$, then

$$\text{curl } \vec{F} = \begin{vmatrix} \vec{i} & \vec{j} & \vec{k} \\ \dfrac{\partial}{\partial x} & \dfrac{\partial}{\partial y} & \dfrac{\partial}{\partial z} \\ xyz & xz & z \end{vmatrix} = (0-x)\vec{i} - (0-xy)\vec{j} + (z-xz)\vec{k}$$

$$= -x\vec{i} + xy\vec{j} + z(1-x)\vec{k}$$

7. If $\vec{F} = \dfrac{1}{x^2 + y^2 + z^2}(x\vec{i} + y\vec{j} + z\vec{k})$, then

$$\text{curl } \vec{F} = \begin{vmatrix} \vec{i} & \vec{j} & \vec{k} \\ \partial/\partial x & \partial/\partial y & \partial/\partial z \\ \dfrac{x}{x^2+y^2+z^2} & \dfrac{y}{x^2+y^2+z^2} & \dfrac{z}{x^2+y^2+z^2} \end{vmatrix}$$

$$= \dfrac{-2xy + 2xy}{(x^2+y^2+z^2)^2}\,\vec{i} - \dfrac{-2xz + 2xz}{(x^2+y^2+z^2)^2}\,\vec{j} + \dfrac{-2xy + 2xy}{(x^2+y^2+z^2)^2}\,\vec{k}$$

$$= \vec{0}$$

11. If $\vec{F}(x,y,z) = (x+y)\vec{i} + (y+z)\vec{j} + (z+x)\vec{k}$, then

$$\text{curl } \vec{F} = \begin{vmatrix} \vec{i} & \vec{j} & \vec{k} \\ \partial/\partial x & \partial/\partial y & \partial/\partial z \\ x+y & y+z & z+x \end{vmatrix} = (0-1)\vec{i} - (1-0)\vec{j} + (0-1)\vec{k}$$

$$= -(\vec{i}+\vec{j}+\vec{k})$$

15. (a) If $\vec{F} = x\vec{i} + y\vec{j}$, then

$$\text{curl } \vec{F} = \begin{vmatrix} \vec{i} & \vec{j} & \vec{k} \\ \partial/\partial x & \partial/\partial y & \partial/\partial z \\ x & y & 0 \end{vmatrix} = 0\vec{i} + 0\vec{j} + 0\vec{k} = \vec{0}$$

Hence, $\vec{F} = x\vec{i} + y\vec{j}$ is conservative.

(b) If $\vec{F} = y\vec{i} + x\vec{j}$, then

$$\text{curl } \vec{F} = \begin{vmatrix} \vec{i} & \vec{j} & \vec{k} \\ \partial/\partial x & \partial/\partial y & \partial/\partial z \\ y & x & 0 \end{vmatrix}$$

$$= 0\vec{i} + 0\vec{j} + (1-1)\vec{k} = \vec{0}$$

Hence, $F = y\vec{i} + x\vec{j}$ is conservative.

(c) If $\vec{F} = y\vec{i} - x\vec{j}$, then

$$\text{curl } \vec{F} = \begin{vmatrix} \vec{i} & \vec{j} & \vec{k} \\ \partial/\partial x & \partial/\partial y & \partial/\partial z \\ y & -x & 0 \end{vmatrix}$$

$$= 0\vec{i} + 0\vec{j} + (1+1)\vec{k} = 2\vec{k}$$

Since $\text{curl } \vec{F} \neq 0$, then $\vec{F}$ is not conservative.

(d) If $\vec{F} = xy\vec{i} + yz\vec{j} + zx\vec{k}$, then

$$\text{curl } \vec{F} = \begin{vmatrix} \vec{i} & \vec{j} & \vec{k} \\ \partial/\partial x & \partial/\partial y & \partial/\partial z \\ xy & yz & zx \end{vmatrix}$$

$$= -y\vec{i} - z\vec{j} - x\vec{k}$$

Since $\text{curl } \vec{F} \neq 0$, we conclude that $\vec{F}$ is not conservative.

(e) If $\vec{F} = yz\vec{i} + zx\vec{j} + xy\vec{k}$, then

$$\text{curl } \vec{F} = \begin{vmatrix} \vec{i} & \vec{j} & \vec{k} \\ \partial/\partial x & \partial/\partial y & \partial/\partial z \\ yz & zx & xy \end{vmatrix}$$

$$= (x-x)\vec{i} - (y-y)\vec{j} + (z-z)\vec{k} = \vec{0}$$

Hence, $\vec{F} = yz\vec{i} + xz\vec{j} + xy\vec{k}$ is conservative.

19. $z = f(x,y) = 1 - x^2 - y^2$ intersects the xy-plane in
the circle $x^2 + y^2 = 1$. Let $x = \cos t$, $y = \sin t$
and $z = 0$. Then $\vec{r}(t) = \cos t\ \vec{i} + \sin t\ \vec{j} + 0\vec{k}$ and
$\oint_C \vec{F} \cdot d\vec{r} = \oint_C [(z-y)\vec{i} + (z+x)\vec{j} - (x+y)\vec{k}](-\sin t\ \vec{i}$

$$+ \cos t\ \vec{j})dt$$

$$= \int_0^{2\pi} [(y-z)\sin t + (x+z)\cos t]dt$$

$$= \int_0^{2\pi} (\sin^2 t + \cos^2 t)dt = \int_0^{2\pi} dt = 2\pi$$

since $z = 0$ on C.

In evaluating $\iint_\Sigma (\text{curl } \vec{F}) \cdot \vec{n}\ dS$, we have

$$\vec{n} = \frac{-f_x\vec{i} - f_y\vec{j} + \vec{k}}{\sqrt{f_x^2 + f_y^2 + 1}} = \frac{2x\vec{i} + 2y\vec{j} + \vec{k}}{\sqrt{4x^2 + 4y^2 + 1}}$$

and

$$\text{curl } \vec{F} = \begin{vmatrix} \vec{i} & \vec{j} & \vec{k} \\ \partial/\partial x & \partial/\partial y & \partial/\partial z \\ z-y & z+x & -x-y \end{vmatrix}$$

$$= (-1-1)\vec{i} - (-1-1)\vec{j} + (1+1)\vec{k} = -2\vec{i} + 2\vec{j} + 2\vec{k}$$

Hence, $(\text{curl } \vec{F}) \cdot \vec{n} = \dfrac{1}{\sqrt{4x^2 + 4y^2 + 1}}(-4x + 4y + 2)$

$$\iint\limits_{\Sigma} (\text{curl } \vec{F}) \cdot \vec{n} \, dS = \iint\limits_{R} (-4x + 4y + 2) \dfrac{\sqrt{4x^2+4y^2+1}}{\sqrt{4x^2+4y^2+1}} \, dx \, dy$$

$$= 4 \int_0^1 \int_0^{\sqrt{1-x^2}} (-4x + 4y + 2) \, dy \, dx$$

$$= 4 \int_0^1 \left[(-4xy + 2y^2 + 2y) \Big|_0^{\sqrt{1-x^2}} \right] dx$$

$$= 4 \int_0^1 (-4x\sqrt{1-x^2} + 2(1-x^2) + 2\sqrt{1-x^2}) \, dx$$

$$= 4 \left[\frac{4}{3}(1-x^2)^{3/2} + 2x - \frac{2}{3}x^3 \right] \Big|_0^1$$

$$+ 8 \int_0^1 \sqrt{1 - x^2} \, dx$$

$$= 4\left(-\frac{4}{3} + \frac{4}{3}\right) + 8\left(\frac{\pi}{4}\right) = 2\pi$$

23. If $\vec{F} = x\vec{i} + (x+y)\vec{j} + (x+y+z)\vec{k}$, then

$$\text{curl } \vec{F} = \begin{vmatrix} \vec{i} & \vec{j} & \vec{k} \\ \partial/\partial x & \partial/\partial y & \partial/\partial z \\ x & x+y & x+y+z \end{vmatrix} = \vec{i} - \vec{j} + \vec{k}$$

Since $z = f(x,y) = 2$, then $\vec{n} = \vec{k}$ is an outer normal. We have

$$\oint_C \vec{F} \cdot d\vec{r} = \iint\limits_{S} (\text{curl } \vec{F}) \cdot \vec{n} \, dS = \iint\limits_{\Sigma} dS = \iint\limits_{R} dx \, dy$$

R is the region in the xy-plane bounded by the circle $x^2 + y^2 = 4\cos^2 t + 4\sin^2 t = 4$. The area of this region is $\pi(2)^2 = 4\pi$.

Hence,

$$\oint_C [x \, dx + (x+y)dy + (x+y+z)dz] = 4\pi$$

Using direct calculation, where $z = 2$ implies $dz = 0$, we have

$$\oint_C \vec{F} \cdot d\vec{r} = \oint_C [x \, dx + (x+y)dy] = \oint_{C_1} [x \, dx + (x+y)dy],$$

where C_1 is the curve in the xy-plane defined by $x = 2 \cos t$, $y = 2 \sin t$, $0 \le t \le 2\pi$. Hence,

$$\oint_C \vec{F} \cdot d\vec{r} = \int_0^{2\pi} [(2 \cos t)(-2 \sin t)$$

$$+ (2 \cos t + 2 \sin t)(2 \cos t)]dt$$

$$= \int_0^{2\pi} 4 \cos^2 t \, dt = 2 \int_0^{2\pi} (1 + \cos 2t)dt$$

$$= 2(t + \frac{1}{2} \sin 2t)\Big|_0^{2\pi} = 4\pi$$

27. If a particle is moved from $(0,0,0)$ to (a,b,c), then we have $\vec{r}(t) = at\vec{i} + bt\vec{j} + ct\vec{k}$, $0 \le t \le 1$, and $\vec{F} \cdot d\vec{r} = [(x+y)\vec{i} + (x-z)\vec{j} + (z-y)\vec{k}] \cdot [a\vec{i} + b\vec{j} + c\vec{k}]dt$

$$= [a(x+y) + b(x-z) + c(z-y)]dt$$

$$= [a(at+bt) + b(at-ct) + c(ct-bt)]dt$$

$$= (a^2 + ab + ab - bc + c^2 - bc)t \, dt$$

$$= (a^2 + 2ab - 2bc + c^2)t \, dt$$

Hence,

$$\oint_C \vec{F} \cdot d\vec{r} = (a^2 + 2ab - 2bc + c^2) \int_0^1 t \, dt$$

$$= \frac{1}{2} a^2 + ab - bc + \frac{1}{2} c^2$$

31. The intersection of the two regions defined by the equations $x + y + z = 0$ and $x^2 + y^2 + z^2 - 1$ is a circle, C, of radius 1 with center at $(0,0,0)$ and tilted 45° in every direction. The major problem is to find a parametric representation for this circle. By the use of spherical coordinates we have $x = \cos(\theta)\sin(\emptyset)$, $y = \sin(\theta)\sin(\emptyset)$ and $z = \cos(\emptyset)$ as points satisfying $x^2 + y^2 + z^2 = 1$. Now put these values into $x + y + z = 0$ and solve for $\tan(\emptyset)$ $= -1/(\sin(\theta)+\cos(\theta))$. Now construct a right triangle with angle $\emptyset$, opposite side -1 and adjacent side $\sin(\theta) + \cos(\theta)$. Then the hypotenuse is $\sqrt{2 + 2\sin(\theta)\cos(\theta)}$. Use these values to replace $\sin(\emptyset)$ and $\cos(\emptyset)$ in x, y and z. We then have, replacing θ with t for convenience,

$$x(t) = \frac{\cos(t)}{\sqrt{2}\sqrt{1 + \sin(t)\cos(t)}}, \quad y(t) = \frac{\sin(t)}{\sqrt{2}\sqrt{1 + \sin(t)\cos(t)}}$$

and $z(t) = -\dfrac{\sin(t) + \cos(t)}{\sqrt{2}\sqrt{1 + \sin(t)\cos(t)}}$, $0 \le t \le 2\pi$.

$$x'(t) = \frac{dx}{dt} = -\frac{2\sin(t) + \cos(t)}{2^{3/2}(1+\sin(t)\cos(t))^{3/2}},$$

$$y'(t) = \frac{dy}{dt} = \frac{2\cos(t) + \sin(t)}{2^{3/2}(1+\sin(t)\cos(t))^{3/2}}$$

and $z'(t) = \dfrac{dz}{dt} = \dfrac{\sin(t) - \cos(t)}{2^{3/2}(1+\sin(t)\cos(t))^{3/2}}$

Now define $\vec{r}(t) = x(t)\vec{i} + y(t)\vec{j} + z(t)\vec{k}$. Then on this curve $d\vec{r} = (x'(t)\vec{i} + y'(t)\vec{j} + z'(t)\vec{k})dt$ and $\vec{F}(x,y,z) = \vec{F}(t) = z(t)\vec{i} + x(t)\vec{j} + y(t)\vec{k}$. We then have $\vec{F}\cdot d\vec{r} = \dfrac{3 + 3\sin(t)\cos(t)}{4(1+\sin(t)\cos(t))}dt$

$= \dfrac{3}{4}\dfrac{1}{1 + \sin(t)\cos(t)}\,dt.$

Thus $\oint_C \vec{F} \cdot d\vec{r} = \dfrac{3}{4} \int_0^{2\pi} \dfrac{dt}{1 + \sin(t)\cos(t)}$

$= \dfrac{3}{8} \int_0^{4\pi} \dfrac{du}{1 + \dfrac{1}{2}\sin(u)} = \dfrac{3}{8} \dfrac{8\sqrt{3}\pi}{3} = \sqrt{3}\pi.$ To evaluate

$\iint_\Sigma \vec{\nabla}\times\vec{F} \cdot \vec{n}$ ds we first find $\vec{\nabla}\times\vec{F}$ to be $\vec{i} + \vec{j} + \vec{k}$.

For Σ we will use the disk bounded by the circle

C and note that $\vec{u} = \dfrac{\vec{i} + \vec{j} + \vec{k}}{\sqrt{3}}$ since the disk is on

the plane $x + y + z = 0$. Therefore $\vec{\nabla}\times\vec{F} \cdot \vec{n} = \sqrt{3}$

$\iint_\Sigma \vec{\nabla}\times\vec{F}\cdot\vec{n}$ ds $= \iint_\Sigma \sqrt{3}$ ds (area of disk) $= \sqrt{3}\pi.$

Miscellaneous Exercises, pp. 1081-1083

3. Considering $f_x = y \cos xy$ and $f_y = x \cos xy$, we

see that $f = \sin xy$ satisfies $\vec{\nabla}f = f_x dx + f_y dy$.

Hence, $\int_C (y \cos xy\ dx + x \cos xy\ dy)$ is independent

of path.

Let C_1: $x = t$, $y = 0$, $0 \le t \le 1$ be the
parametric equation of the line from $(0,0)$ to $(1,0)$,
and let C_2: $x = 1$, $y = t$, $0 \le t \le 1$ be the line
from $(1,0)$ to $(1,1)$. Then,

$\int_{C_1} (y \cos xy\ dx + x \cos xy\ dy) = \int_0^1 0\ dt = 0$ and

$\int_{C_2} (y \cos xy\ dx + x \cos xy\ dy) = \int_0^1 [t \cos t(0\ dt)$

$+ \cos t\ dt] = \int_0^1 \cos t\ dt = \sin t \Big|_0^1 = \sin 1$

Then, $\int_C = \int_{C_1} + \int_{C_2} = \sin 1$

7. Since $f(x,y) = e^x \sin y$ has the gradient

$\vec{\nabla}f = (e^x \sin y)\vec{i} + (e^x \cos y)\vec{j}$, then the integral

is independent of path and

$$\int_C (e^x \sin y \, dx + e^x \cos y \, dy) = f(1,1) - f(0,0)$$

$$= e \sin 1$$

11. If $\vec{F}$ is directed toward the origin and has

magnitude inversly proportional to the square of the

distance to the origin, then

$$\vec{F}(x,y,z) = \frac{-k}{(x^2+y^2+z^2)^{3/2}} (x\vec{i}+y\vec{j}+z\vec{k}) \text{ for some } k > 0.$$

$\vec{F}$ is obviously directed toward the origin and one

may readily verify that its magnitude satisfies the

inverse square requirement. Since

$$\text{curl } \vec{F} = \begin{vmatrix} \vec{i} & \vec{j} & \vec{k} \\ \dfrac{\partial}{\partial x} & \dfrac{\partial}{\partial y} & \dfrac{\partial}{\partial z} \\ \dfrac{-kx}{(x^2+y^2+z^2)^{3/2}} & \dfrac{-ky}{(x^2+y^2+z^2)^{3/2}} & \dfrac{-kz}{(x^2+y^2+z^2)^{3/2}} \end{vmatrix}$$

$$= \frac{1}{(x^2+y^2+z^2)^{5/2}}[(3kzy-3kyz)\vec{i} - (3kzx-3kxz)\vec{j}$$

$+ (3kyx-3kxy)\vec{k}] = 0\vec{i} + 0\vec{j} + 0\vec{k} = 0$, $\vec{F}$ is

conservative. A potential f of $\vec{F}$ would have

$$\frac{\partial f}{\partial x} = \frac{-kx}{(x^2+y^2+z^2)^{3/2}} \text{ so}$$

$$f(x,y,z) = \int \frac{-kx}{(x^2+y^2+z^2)^{3/2}} \, dx + g(y,z)$$

$$= \frac{k}{(x^2+y^2+z^2)^{1/2}} + g(y,z) \text{ for some function g.}$$

Now $\frac{\partial f}{\partial y} = \frac{-ky}{(x^2+y^2+z^2)^{3/2}} + \frac{\partial}{\partial y} g(x,y)$. Comparison

of this with $\frac{-ky}{(x^2+y^2+z^2)^{3/2}}$ requires that $\frac{\partial y}{\partial y} = 0$.

Letting $g(y,z) = h(z)$ we have

$f(x,y,z) = \frac{k}{(x^2+y^2+z^2)^{1/2}} + h(z)$. Then

$\frac{\partial f}{\partial z} = \frac{-kz}{(x^2+y^2+z^2)^{3/2}} + h'(z)$. Comparison of this

with $\frac{-kz}{(x^2+y^2+z^2)^{3/2}}$ implies that $h'(z) = 0$.

If we let $h(z) = 0$ we have

$f(x,y,z) = \frac{k}{(x^2+y^2+z^2)^{1/2}}$ as a potential of the

force $\vec{F}$.

15. If $P = x - y$ and $Q = x + y$, then $\frac{\partial Q}{\partial x} = 1$ and

$\frac{\partial P}{\partial y} = -1$. Using Green's theorem, we have

$$\oint_C [(x-y)dx + (x+y)dy] = \iint_R (1+1)dx\ dy = 2 \iint_R dx\ dy$$

Since the area of an ellipse with center at the
origin and intercepts a and b is $A = ab\pi$, the
area of the given ellipse is $A = (2)(3)\pi = 6\pi$.
Hence,

$$\oint_C [(x-y)dx + (x+y)dy] = 2(6\pi) = 12\pi$$

19. For the hypocycloid $x = a \cos^3 t$, $y = a \sin^3 t$, $0 \leq t \leq \dfrac{\pi}{2}$, we have

$$A = \iint\limits_{R} dx\, dy = \oint\limits_{C} x\, dy, \quad \text{using} \quad Q = x,\ P = 0,$$

and $\iint\limits_{R} \left(\dfrac{\partial Q}{\partial x} - \dfrac{\partial P}{\partial y} \right) dA = \oint\limits_{C} (P\, dx + Q\, dy)$. Hence,

$$A = \int_{0}^{\pi/2} (a \cos^3 t)(3a \sin^2 t \cos t)\, dt$$

$$= 3a^2 \int_{0}^{\pi/2} \cos^4 t \sin^2 t\, dt$$

$$= 3a^2 \int_{0}^{\pi/2} \cos^4 t (1 - \cos^2 t)\, dt$$

$$= 3a^2 \int_{0}^{\pi/2} \cos^4 t\, dt - 3a^2 \int_{0}^{\pi/2} \cos^6 t\, dt$$

$$= \frac{3}{4} a^2 \int_{0}^{\pi/2} (1 + \cos 2t)^2\, dt - \frac{3a^2}{8} \int_{0}^{\pi/2} (1 + \cos 2t)^3\, dt$$

$$= \frac{3}{4} a^2 \int_{0}^{\pi/2} [1 + 2 \cos 2t + \frac{1}{2} + \frac{1}{2} \cos 4t]\, dt$$

$$\quad - \frac{3}{8} a^2 \int_{0}^{\pi/2} [1 + 3 \cos 2t + (\frac{3}{2} + \frac{3}{2} \cos 4t) + \cos^3 2t]\, dt$$

$$= \frac{3}{4} a^2 (\frac{3}{2} t + \sin 2t + \frac{1}{8} \sin 4t) \Big|_{0}^{\pi/2}$$

$$\quad - \frac{3}{8} a^2 (\frac{5}{2} t + \frac{3}{2} \sin 2t + \frac{3}{8} \sin 4t) \Big|_{0}^{\pi/2}$$

$$\quad - \frac{3}{8} a^2 \int_{0}^{\pi/2} \cos^3 2t\, dt$$

$$= \frac{9}{16} \pi a^2 - \frac{15}{32} \pi a^2 - \frac{3}{8} a^2 \int_{0}^{\pi/2} \cos 2t (1 - \sin^2 2t)\, dt$$

$$= \frac{3}{32} \pi a^2 - \frac{3}{8} a^2 \int_0^{\pi/2} \cos 2t \, dt$$

$$+ \frac{3}{8} a^2 \int_0^{\pi/2} \sin^2 2t \cos 2t \, dt$$

or $\quad A = \dfrac{3}{32} \pi a^2 - \dfrac{3}{16} a^2 \sin 2t \Big|_0^{\pi/2} + \dfrac{1}{16} a^2 \sin^3 2t \Big|_0^{\pi/2}$

$$= \frac{3}{32} \pi a^2$$

Also,

$$\int_C x^2 dy = \int_0^{\pi/2} a^2 \cos^6 t (3a \sin^2 t \cos t) dt$$

$$= 3a^3 \int_0^{\pi/2} \cos^7 t \sin^2 t \, dt$$

$$= 3a^3 \int_0^{\pi/2} \sin^2 t (1 - \sin^2 t)^3 \cos t \, dt$$

$$= 3a^3 \int_0^{\pi/2} (\sin^2 t - 3 \sin^4 t + 3 \sin^6 t - \sin^8 t) \cos t \, dt$$

$$= 3a^3 \left(\frac{1}{3} \sin^3 t - \frac{3}{5} \sin^5 t + \frac{3}{7} \sin^7 t - \frac{1}{9} \sin^9 t \right) \Big|_0^{\pi/2}$$

$$= 3a^3 \left(\frac{1}{3} - \frac{3}{5} + \frac{3}{7} - \frac{1}{9} \right) = \frac{48}{315} a^3,$$

and

$$\int_C y^2 dx = \int_0^{\pi/2} a^2 \sin^6 t (-3a \cos^2 t \sin t) dt$$

$$= -3a^3 \int_0^{\pi/2} \sin^7 t \cos^2 t \, dt$$

$$= -3a^3 \int_0^{\pi/2} \cos^2 t(1-\cos^2 t)^3 \sin t \; dt$$

$$= -3a^3 \int_0^{\pi/2} (\cos^2 t - 3\cos^4 t + 3\cos^6 t - \cos^8 t)\sin t \; dt$$

$$= 3a^3 \left(\frac{1}{3}\cos^3 t - \frac{3}{5}\cos^5 t + \frac{3}{7}\cos^7 t - \frac{1}{9}\cos^9 t\right)\Big|_0^{\pi/2}$$

$$= 3a^3 \left[0 - \left(\frac{1}{3} - \frac{3}{5} + \frac{3}{7} - \frac{1}{9}\right)\right] = \frac{-48}{315} a^3$$

Hence, $\bar{x} = \frac{1}{2A}\int_C x^2 dy = \frac{256a}{315\pi}$, and $\bar{y} = \frac{-1}{2a}\int y^2 dx$

$$= \frac{256a}{315\pi}$$

23. We have $\rho(x,y,z) = k\sqrt{x^2 + y^2 + z^2} = ka$. Hence, the mass m is given by

$$m = \iint_S \rho dS = 2\iint_R \rho\sqrt{f_x^2 + f_y^2 + 1} \; dx \; dy,$$

where R is the circle $x^2 + y^2 = a^2$, $f(x,y) = z = \sqrt{a^2 - x^2 + y^2}$, and we multiply $\iint_R$ by two to include the lower half. Thus,

$$\sqrt{f_x^2 + f_y^2 + 1} = \frac{a}{\sqrt{a^2 - x^2 - y^2}} \quad \text{and}$$

$$m = 2ka^2 \iint_R \frac{dx \; dy}{\sqrt{a^2 - x^2 - y^2}} = 8ka^2 \int_0^{\pi/2} \int_0^a \frac{1}{\sqrt{a^2 - r^2}} r \; dr \; d\theta$$

$$= 8ka^2 \int_0^{\pi/2} [-\sqrt{a^2 - r^2}\Big|_{r=0}^{a}] d\theta = 8ka^3 \int_0^{\pi/2} d\theta = 4k\pi a^3$$

27. Suppose the velocity F of a fluid flow in space is a constant, say $\vec{F} = \vec{C} = a\vec{i} + b\vec{j} + c\vec{k}$. If S is any closed surface in space, the flux through S is given by

$\iint\limits_{S} \rho\vec{F} \cdot \vec{n} \ dS = \rho\iint\limits_{S} \vec{C} \cdot \vec{n} \ dS.$ However, using the

divergence theorem we have

$\iint\limits_{S} \vec{C} \cdot \vec{n} \ dS = \iiint\limits_{T} (\text{div } \vec{C}) dV$

The divergence of a vector $\vec{F} = P\vec{i} + Q\vec{j} + R\vec{k}$ is
div $\vec{F} = Px + Qy + Rz.$ Hence, div $\vec{C} = 0.$ Thus,
the flux is

$\rho \iint\limits_{S} \vec{C} \cdot \vec{n} \ dS = \rho\iiint\limits_{T}(\text{div } \vec{C})dV = \rho\iiint\limits_{T} 0 \ dV = 0$

31. We have $\int_C = \int_{C_1} + \int_{C_2} + \int_{C_3}$ where C_1 is the
line from $(1,0,0)$ to $(0,1,0)$,
C_2 is the line from $(0,1,0)$
to $(0,0,1)$, and C_3 is the
line from $(0,0,1)$ to $(1,0,0)$.
Parametrically we can define
C_1, C_2, and C_3 as follows:

C_1: $x = 1 - t,$ $y = t,$ $z = 0,$ $0 \le t \le 1$
    $[dx = -dt,$ $dy = dt,$ $dz = 0 \ dt]$

C_2: $x = 0,$ $y = 1 - t,$ $z = t;$ $0 \le t \le 1$
    $[dx = 0 \ dt,$ $dy = -dt,$ $dz = dt]$

C_3: $x = t,$ $y = 0,$ $z = 1 - t,$ $0 \le t \le 1$
    $[dx = dt,$ $dy = 0 \ dt,$ $dz = -dt]$

Hence, $\int_{C_1} [(x-y)dx + (y-z)dy + (z-x)dz]$

$= \int_0^1 [(1-2t)(-1) + t + 0]dt = \int_0^1 (3t-1)dt$

$= (\frac{3}{2} t^2 - t)\Big|_0^1 = \frac{1}{2}$

$\int_{C_2} [(x-y)dx + (y-z)dy + (z-x)dz]$

$= \int_0^1 [0 + (1-2t)(-1) + t]dt = \int_0^1 (3t-1)dt = \frac{1}{2}$

$\int_{C_3} [(x-y)dx + (y-z)dy + (z-x)dz]$

$= \int_0^1 [t + 0 + (1-2t)(-1)]dt = \int_0^1 (3t-1)dt = \frac{1}{2}$

Hence, $\int_C Pdx + Qdy + Rdz = \frac{1}{2} + \frac{1}{2} + \frac{1}{2} = \frac{3}{2}$